BEYOND
SOUTH GATE

by Carroll F. Rader

Cover design by Jane Brannen
Published by The Francis Asbury Society

ISBN 978-0-915143-23-8
Printed in the United States of America

To order this book, go to www.francisasburysociety.com or contact:

Francis Asbury Society
PO Box 7
Wilmore, KY 40390-0007
859-858-4222

Dedicated to Everett N. Hunt, Jr.,
whose academic research notes
enabled the telling of this story.

Preface

Ella Appenzeller incarnates the American Protestant missionary woman. She was one link in a long, strong, flawed chain of sent ones, neither much better or worse than most of the others, although perhaps being first into a country makes even an ordinary individual special in a sense. Be that as it may, she served, as did those bearing better known names like Carey, Judson, and Livingstone— men and women who made horrendous errors in Jesus' name, but who burned that name into the hearts and minds and cultures of nations.

We honor and revere these missionaries, put them safely up on pedestals where they won't bother us with their committed humanity, but we seldom crawl inside their skins and look out through their eyes. We don't know what makes them laugh or what they really think of the people to whom they devote their lives.

Do they ever go to parties? Have fun? Find someone other than their mates interesting or attractive?

Are missionaries truly spiritual giants, as we want to believe? Do they always handle problems and opportunities in a biblical fashion, unfailingly controlled by the power of the Holy Spirit?

Ella pioneered mission in Korea with her husband, Henry. Her diaries did not survive, if indeed she kept any. But some of Henry's did, and so did letters, sermons and talks, reports and articles. From these and from my own thirty-plus years in mission, I have fabricated in the pages that follow her thoughts, attitudes and reactions. You can watch her grow and change from a naive bride into a survivor of cholera epidemics and political upheaval, one who copes with a husband's long absences and finally, his early death.

Ella's chronology is correct in this work of fiction, as are the major events that shaped the living and the working of the Appenzellers. Her reaction to her environment and the challenges she grappled with are as I imagined them to be, but imagining was not difficult because I, insignificant in that long chain of missionaries from another time than Ella's, lived in Seoul for a couple of decades and know that some of the issues the pioneers confronted were not that different for us a hundred years later.

I hope you will open your mind and imagination to Ella and her friends. Let them represent all of us to whom God said go, and we went. Through them, let missionaries be less than icons and more like real people walking the Christian way, serving the Master as best we can in whatever place He puts us. Walk with us for a time through the pages of this book and as Ella's story unfolds, let her represent the missionary you know in Europe, South America, Africa or Asia. Get to know her, or him, better. Cry with her, laugh with him, kick the furniture in frustration or throw back your head and bellow at the ceiling with joy.

Whatever you do, though, don't ignore us. You have a crucial role to play in the task of world evangelization, even if you don't set foot outside your home territory and even if you have no funds you can contribute to this cause. You can care, and when you care you pray. When you pray you participate in the going, the translating, the persecution, the setbacks and the triumphs. How does the Bible put it about sharing alike, those who go into battle and those who stay by the stuff? As you read these pages you participate in mission, that inexplicable, inefficient, God-ordained plan to tell the world about His Son, Jesus Christ.

If I rise on the wings of the dawn,
if I settle on the far side of the sea,
even there your hand will guide me,
your right hand will hold me fast.

—*Psalm 139:9, 10 (NIV)*

Prologue

People as old as I am must grapple with an aberration that refuses to go away. I've been staring at the stack of boxes in the front hall for three days and rather than do the practical thing and summon someone to deliver them to New York, I stand looking at them and wondering where my life has gone, gone so quickly that I never sensed it slipping through my fingers. Wasn't it only last week that my darling Henry wrote all the letters stacked in those boxes and read to me his diary entries that trumpeted his triumphs or vented his spleen at the difficulties, like the way Koreans do business or give directions? Now those letters and diaries are headed to the attic at mission headquarters; "valuable historical documents," they call them.

What do they know of value when it comes to the lives of Ella and Henry Appenzeller? About the same amount—which is nothing—that they know about the disagreement between the wrinkled granny in my mirror and the slim-waisted, wide-eyed bride who still inhabits my creaking body. Even yet she wants to sing and run and wear bright colors, to laugh at the wrong times. Why didn't she slow down and dry up along with her bones and skin?

There's no point, though, in being querulous and negative. We embarked upon our Korean adventure in ignorance, armed only with our youth and our desire—well, Henry's mainly—to accomplish something in the name of God. And I'd say we didn't do too badly, all things considered. Korea certainly left her fingerprints all over us, some of them sweet-scented and gentle but more often acquired by her rude, rough touch. Even the getting there almost did us in.

And when I left that land for the last time I was certainly a different person from when we arrived.

Feelings aside, I will eventually send for the delivery man and he'll take away these boxes, but he won't be able to lay a finger on the adventures, the mistakes and triumphs, the choices, good and bad, we made, or on the fact that we went to Korea as the first of many and we made a difference in that lovely little country—and we all survived. Well, almost all of us.

And sure as Seoul's South Gate stands, that which my Henry planted across the mountains and down the coasts of the Land of the Morning Calm will flourish beyond our most pious dreams.

South Gate. Sturdy and square, with her tipped-up roof corners, symbolizes for me my life in Korea. Through her stony heart I rode at sundown when we first arrived in Seoul, young, untried, unaware. And because she stood so near the home we finally found, I carried each of our four children out to see her and the crowds always clustered there at the main entrance to the city.

We picnicked and argued, wept and laughed under the pines outside the gate. We shopped in the market that sprawls in her shadow inside the wall. I miss her now that I can't go back, but she lives on inside my head even though I've moved forever beyond her dear old presence.

South Gate remains the same, and so do I. Each of us shows the tracks of the years, it's true, and each of us has participated in more than our share of trauma, change and pain. Yet her square-cut stones are at heart the same as when her builders lifted them into place centuries ago.

And me? I'm wiser, calmer, older, yet the same girl laughs inside me and looks out through the same eyes at the world and its wonders.

And I know that one of the greatest evidences of God's wisdom is that He doesn't allow us to see what lies along the path ahead. He knew, and now so do I, which if I'd known half of what I now know, I would not have walked so willingly to meet Henry Appenzeller at the altar on our wedding day, nor would I have traveled with him to Korea.

But I did, and because we both went to Korea, we two changed forever.

Contents

Chapter 1

Into the Unknown

No girl knows what she's getting into when she pulls that white veil across her face and meets her man at the altar. Neither did I.

All I knew was that Henry had a square chin, strong arms and a heart overrun with dreams of changing the world for God. So, I married him on December 17, 1884, a simple act with profound consequences—for me and for the world.

We had no wedding trip. Instead, we spent those normally secluded private honeymoon days with parents, packing into trunks and cases our clothes, books, supplies and wedding gifts, preparing to embark for Korea so Henry could pursue his dreams and change the world. And I, knowing less than nothing about Christian vocation, thought only of staying as close as possible to the man I loved. One frigid morning in January we boarded the westbound train in Lancaster, Pennsylvania, after wrenching ourselves away from family and the friends who came to wave us on our way. My brother, Byron, held me tight for a long moment.

"Ah, Ella, I hate to let you go. Korea seems so far."

I sobbed on his shoulder, the only reply I could manage. He looked at Henry who tugged on my elbow, anxious to be off on his great adventure.

"You take care of my sister, sir, or you'll answer to me." Byron tried to make it sound humorous but the joke fell flat.

Henry looked long into his eyes and then with his arm about my shoulders said, "I promised to care for her until death do us part. You have my word."

Byron nodded and stepped back. Henry and I mounted the train's iron steps, turning to wave as the whistle blew and the wheels began to inch along the rails. Our families shrank and disappeared as the train gathered speed. For better or for worse, our journey had begun.

―――――――――――■―――――――――――

Liberated from another train I can't remember how many days later in San Francisco, we descended another set of iron steps to be greeted by William and Loulie Scranton, the doctor and wife with whom we were to travel to Korea. William's widowed mother also accompanied us and I had no idea at the time what a formidable prospect that would be, for she was not at the station when we arrived.

I took to Loulie at once. About my age—which means, I decided much later, too young to have any sense at all, either one of us—she was dark-haired, petite and quick with a ready smile. Deeply awed by her doctor husband and by her mother-in-law, she didn't talk much except when we were alone. I knew from the moment I met her that we could be good friends, and the Lord knew we would need each other in the days to come.

The five of us sailed from San Francisco on February 2nd. Henry had watched our goods being loaded onto the ship while I lounged in the hotel room, enjoying the solitude and pondering the whole business of marriage. When the task was finished, he burst into the room all windblown and smelling of salty seas.

"Ella, just think!" he shouted. "We won't see our stuff again until we unpack it in Korea!" He grabbed me about the waist and lifted me up until I could look down on the top of his tousled head.

"I'm not sure—"

"Don't you see?" he interrupted. "Our journey to Korea's begun at last. We're on our way. Stowing our things away in the ship's hold let me see it is finally happening…"

On and on he went even after he put me down and we sat together on the side of the bed. I was beginning to learn that Henry was a talker. Conversation with him required little skill on my part. But he finally wound down and lay back on the pillows. With outstretched arms he invited me to join him in learning more about the love that flamed between us.

Talk my husband did as we sailed ever west toward the Orient. If he wasn't talking, either to me or to anyone else within earshot, he wrote in his journal. He didn't offer to show it to me and I didn't much care, for our voyage was turning into the honeymoon we never had back in December. So lovely were those days and nights we shared. How glad I was to be sailing with Henry, with his square chin and strong arms, it didn't matter where we were going so long as we went there together.

In mid-February for the first time I heard my husband preach. It was quite good, I thought. The topic was fine— something about Jesus sleeping through a storm in an open fishing boat and trusting the Creator of the wind and waves—but what I enjoyed most was watching Henry stand tall and handsome, a half smile on his face, his eyes glowing with enthusiasm. Who wouldn't agree to anything he suggested when he looked like that?

A few days later Loulie and I stood at the rail staring at the waves and talking together. I was fussing as usual with my flyaway yellow hair when I noticed that one small patch of the horizon looked different from the rest, almost like the dark smudges I get under my eyes when I'm tired.

"Look, Loulie," I said, abandoning my impossible curls and pointing a gloved finger at the dark patch. "What is that, do you think?"

Loulie peered into the distance for a moment, then said, "Do you suppose it's land? We're due in Japan soon."

We giggled and hugged each other, eager to be free from the tossing, heaving ship that had given us both our first taste of the miseries of seasickness.

While we danced and chattered, both Henry and Mrs. Scranton paced up and down the deck, quiet for once and lost in thought, probably busy praying over the events ahead of us. Loulie's mother-in-law adopted a serious, solemn look at all times and had the curious habit of looking you over before responding to the simplest pleasantry you ventured. This always made me wonder, "Why did I say that? She's surely displeased now and I shall be punished." I took to avoiding her.

Next morning when I woke, Henry was already gone. "Honeymoon's over," I thought. He'd not left me before, but on this morning I couldn't compete with his first glimpse of Yokohama Bay.

I dressed in a rush, pinned my uncooperative hair into a lopsided bun and went up on deck where a cold damp wind whipped about great soft flakes of snow. At the rail I looked below at half-dressed Japanese men—at least I assumed they were Japanese for they surely weren't Americans—balancing on sinewy legs in tossing little boats. This was more skin than I'd ever seen on anyone except my husband so I stared, hard, until Mrs. Scranton's authoritarian voice erupted in my ear.

"Good morning, Ella. Are you prepared to climb down this ladder when we disembark?"

I started violently and I know my face flamed red, caught staring at the unclad workmen below by her, of all people.

"Ladder? You mean this?" My darting eyes focused belatedly on a rope ladder hanging over the side and tossing in the wind. Dear Lord, surely not.

"Yes, indeed. That represents our means of departure from this ship."

"But how?"

"I'm sure they will tell us when the time comes." Her reply carried such an edge, or so it seemed to me. Was I guilty of some misstep?

Tell us they did, and when my turn came to clamber over the rail and commit myself to that flimsy, wavering web of twisted hemp, I wondered, not for the last time, what had possessed us to leave the safety and good sense of the United States. Henry preceded me down the ladder and as soon as he could reach me, he lifted me down the rest of the way even though the Japanese workmen snickered and shook their heads. What did they find so amusing in a man acting like a gentleman in such a situation, I wondered, for I was as yet untutored in their culture.

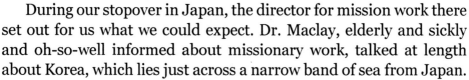

During our stopover in Japan, the director for mission work there set out for us what we could expect. Dr. Maclay, elderly and sickly and oh-so-well informed about missionary work, talked at length about Korea, which lies just across a narrow band of sea from Japan.

"I'll not be able to come over and assist you in any way," he told the Scrantons and us. "Letters take at least a month between Seoul and Tokyo, so quick advice or direction will not be available to you."

I peeked at Will Scranton and at Henry as Maclay spoke and they both were struggling to keep the pleasure off their faces. They obviously didn't want any advice and direction. They couldn't wait to go it alone, to try themselves against whatever we would find. Henry sat straight and listened politely, but I could sense he was eager to seize responsibility and run with it.

"Korea is in the throes of upheaval and conflict," Maclay droned on. "Both Japan and China entertain colonial aspirations and want to control her. They may even be willing to use force to do so. War could break out at any moment. Truth be told, this is not a good time to go there, especially taking women. I would prefer you to stay here until matters settle down."

Neither Will Scranton nor Henry responded to that suggestion. I looked across at Loulie, seated by her physician husband. She gazed back at me, and then she lifted her slim shoulders in a tiny shrug. She, too, knew the men would not wait if they could avoid it. How much trouble can politics create, after all? Surely we'd be all right.

Chapter 2

Culture and Cuisine

Henry and I spent almost a month, a long dreadful month, in Japan before finally going on to Korea. He trailed around with the other men peering in at schools and churches and printing presses. I didn't fare so well and Henry caught me weeping in my pillow one afternoon just before dinner.

"Ella? What is it, darling? What's the matter?" He pulled me close and whispered in my ear, a form of speech we'd adopted to avoid being overheard through flimsy guestroom doors.

"Oh, Henry," I sobbed. "I'm so...so miserable...."

"Tell me."

"I'm tired of being company all the time. This is the third spare room we've stayed in here. I've never even cooked a meal for you, ever! And I want to unpack our wedding gifts and for us to be at home, just you and me. I feel like someone's indigent cousin being handed around from house to house."

I snuffled on through my litany of woes and for once Henry didn't talk; he just listened. Finally the comfort of his strong arms and broad shoulders seeped into me, plus I ran out of things to complain about. After all, how many "I wants" can you stuff into one self-pity recital?

"Tired of trains and boats and guestrooms, are you?" he murmured against my hair. "How would you feel about boarding just one more ship next Monday if I promise to load all our baggage on it, too?"

"To Korea?" I grabbed his arms and shook him and I'm afraid I shrieked it out, ignoring our room's paper-thin walls. "Seriously, Henry. Are we going?"

"We sail at dawn."

Suddenly a warm sun shone in our borrowed room and I knew that if I looked hard enough I could find a rainbow bending round the ugly mahogany wardrobe towering in the corner. A home at last, a place of our own where I could finally be a wife in all the ways my mother taught me, plus some I learned on my own. It was joy unspeakable.

Nagoya Maru, our rusty, tubby ship—a coaster they called it—plowed through the greasy waters of Yokohama Bay early Monday morning. At the beginning of our voyage we shared a dining table with a delegation of Korean officials and a German diplomat and advisor to the Korean king, Herr Moellendorff, who were returning from offering apologies to the Japanese government for some unpleasantness that took place in a Korean post office last December. I didn't pay close attention to Henry's discussion with Herr Moellendorff about the issue because I was mesmerized by the Koreans' attack on the menu. Communication was difficult between the Japanese steward who spoke rudimentary English and the Koreans, who did not.

"What you eat, suh?"

The first Korean official thus approached waved at the bill of fare, nodded and said, "Neh" (my first Korean word; "neh" means yes).

"Which one, suh?"

"Neh."

"All of it, suh?"

"Neh."

And so forth through the entire group. The steward's face remained unchanged, his eyes on his order ticket, but I noticed a faint reddish wash of color on his ivory-hued cheekbones as, task completed, he turned and disappeared into the kitchen.

"Can you believe it?" Henry chortled later in our cabin. "And they ate it all. How did they do that?"

"This ship is terribly unsteady," I replied. "Imagine how unsettling it could be on an overstuffed stomach."

As we chuckled and shook our heads, a dreadful sound poured through the wall. Such a retching and coughing and wailing I'd never heard. The next morning we dined alone.

Henry talked Asian politics while patrolling the deck with the opinionated Moellendorff. He thought the German knew the Korean situation well.

"China and Japan are struggling for control of Korea," he quoted Herr Moellendorff. "But the United States remains disinterested in the affair, so coming from the U.S. will be in our favor." I found it intriguing that disinterest, which we don't like when it is applied to us personally, was perceived as positive in politics.

Another encounter with Herr Moellendorff shed enlightenment on a different matter. Traveling with us was a Korean student, Mr. Suh, whom we'd met in Japan and who was trying to teach us the Korean language. The four of us were sitting together in the social room when Suh rose to go at about 9 p.m.

"Please excuse me. I shall say good night." He bowed politely to Herr Moellendorff. Then he turned to Henry. "Good night, sir. I hope you rest well." Again, a polite bow.

Suh then turned and left the room, ignoring me as if I were just another piece of scuffed furniture on the Nagoya Maru. As Suh walked out the door, Henry began to swell with anger and outrage, for his manners were impeccable and his attitudes about gallantry toward ladies engraved on his soul. For a moment he froze, unsure of what to do. After all, dueling was outlawed long ago. Red-faced and pop-eyed, he began to sputter and huff.

"Now, now, my friend," Herr Moellendorff soothed. "You must understand the way things are on this side of the world." He glanced at me uneasily and then haltingly explained Oriental attitudes toward women. According to him, we were regarded as inferior and troublesome, useful at times—in the kitchen and bedroom, he implied—but not nearly so worthy as men. I sensed that Herr Moellendorff approved of the system.

"Uh, gentlemen," I rose, red-faced myself if truth be told, "please excuse me. I'm a bit tired and will retire." I knew the men could discuss Korean attitudes toward women more comfortably without me, plus I'd taken in about all I could digest for one day. What in the world had we gotten ourselves into? What kind of life could I look forward to among these strange people? I wasn't sure I wanted anything to do with them if this was the kind of treatment I could expect.

We lost Herr Moellendorff and his overstuffed Korean delegation when we docked in Kobe, and we gained the Reverend Horace G. Underwood, a young man of medium height with a strong voice and sandy hair that tended to stand upright in the back. Underwood and Henry found plenty to talk about as we left the Japanese coast and chugged across the straits toward Korea. I did not join in their conversations as much as I might have for I felt a bit unwell. Dull headaches and a queasy stomach marred my mornings, but I counted on the fresh sea air to clear it up.

It didn't clear as I'd hoped, but a stop in Pusan distracted me momentarily. Pusan lies at the southern tip of the Korean peninsula and to be able to look at our adopted country excited Henry beyond description. He paced and grinned and scribbled in his pocket-sized journal, squinting across at the shore and pointing out to anyone who would listen every hummock and hovel he spied. Untouched by his lofty goals, I ignored his words, satisfied to gaze at him instead. God love him, he was a fine looking man, so full of energy and spirit, with that wonderful squared-off chin giving his face such strength. How I loved him even though my physical difficulties quenched any enthusiasm I might possibly have shared with him at seeing Korea. My sole hope was to get off that wretched little tub of a ship.

When we docked in Pusan, temporary relief met us. "Ella, we're invited to tour the town," Henry told me. "Mr. Lovatt, the port customs officer, is offering to show us around."

"Let's do it." I struggled to show a little cheer and interest. Surely a walk around on dry land would make me feel better.

"Ella, I've been praying..." Henry talked while I smoothed my hair and dug out a shawl from our cabin baggage.

"Yes, I know, dear." He often prayed. Enough for both of us.

"...praying that among those hills and valleys we see from the deck, Christian churches might be built and that the fires of charity and good works be lighted all over the land."

It was a profound and powerful sentiment he expressed that day, especially when I consider all that took place in the years to come.

But all I could think of then was my own misery.

Under Mr. Lovatt's guidance we walked across plowed fields, up steep hills, through brush and over enough stones that my thoughts turned back to New England. I saw women washing clothes on rocks beside a stream. They beat the white garments with a stick and then swished them about in the water before spreading them out on the hillside grass to dry. Their faces were brown and leathery from the sun and each wore her black hair pulled back and rolled into a bun on the nape of her neck.

How will I do laundry when we finally have our own home, I wondered. Shall I have to kneel by a stream and pound it on a rock?

During our wanderings we came upon a small temple. While Mr. Lovatt explained the ins and outs of Buddhism to Henry, I wandered across the main room—do they call it a sanctuary as we Christians do? I wondered—and looked closely at the sticks of incense burning before the high altar. Perched with his head among the rafters sat the golden Buddha, overweight and immobile, with eyes half closed and hands resting, palms up, upon his knees.

A woman with a tiny girl in tow left her shoes at the door and walked up to face the Buddha. I couldn't understand what she said to the little girl—our language lessons hadn't carried me that far yet—but I watched as she pressed those dimpled hands together and showed the child how to clap. The clap, I learned later, was meant to attract the god's attention and to notify him that she was going to pray. Then the woman pushed on the back of her daughter's head to make her bow, but the little one was so caught up staring at us foreigners that I'm afraid her worship lesson didn't amount to much that day.

Back on ship, Henry tossed and rolled in his bunk as we wallowed north along the Korean coast. I couldn't sleep, sick again, so I got up and went out on deck in search of fresh air to ease my nausea. There it hit me.

Could my illness be caused by pregnancy? What if I'm expecting a child? My heart pounded at the thought. A baby! A boy with Henry's chin? A tiny girl with blond curls like mine? How lovely, how wonderful!

How awkward.

Back to my pitching bunk I crawled, carrying my divided heart with me. I wanted to pounce on Henry, pummel him awake and share my thoughts, but the poor dear was almost as sick of sailing as I was so I let him sleep as I thought and wondered and planned alone.

———————◆———————

Next day I gave up and stayed in bed. Food smelled and tasted horrible. Nothing, not even sips of water stayed down. Henry was kind. His problems came and went and I'm sure he thought I overplayed the fragile female role by more than a little. He never rebuked me, however.

Fresh air helped, so I kept the porthole open even though rain and the odd splash of sea water came in on my bed. Henry spread his new raincoat over me to keep me dry. My major diversion between waves of nausea was to gather little pools of water in its folds and pour them out through the open porthole.

I still hadn't told my husband of my suspicions regarding my condition. Even that required more strength than I could muster. He plodded off to every meal, morning, noon and night, bringing back with him some morsel to tantalize my appetite and settle my stomach.

To please him I ate the stuff and then, pleasing or not, threw it right back up again.

But at last we arrived in Chemulpo, our port of destination on April 5, 1885. We were finally delivered from rusty steamers and heaving seas on a gray and dreary day just like all the rest in recent memory.

"Ella! Ella! We're here! We're getting off. Hurry, come and see!" Henry's face shone with such joy and anticipation that for an instant he seemed like a stranger to me. Who was this man shouting at me? How could he be caught in such emotional extremes when I, in the same place and situation, feel nothing?

"I'm coming, darling." I forced a smile across my face as I staggered toward him. "Will someone bring our things?"

We moved up onto the deck, Henry bounding while I tottered. Near our rusty tub of a ship, the USS Ossipee lay at anchor and the sight of an American warship with her Stars and Stripes whipping in the wind laid a profound silence on us both. We stared at the flag, the English letters on the ship's side, the U.S. Navy uniforms scurrying across her deck. Henry spoke first.

"There! That should do us some good."

Until that moment I did not know my cheerful, positive-thinking husband needed good done for him, but when he admitted to his spirits being lifted by the sight of Old Glory, I felt closer to him than I had in a long while.

"There'll be no one to meet us here as we had in Japan," I murmured.

He looked down at me, and then squeezed my hand. "We have arrived in the regions beyond," he said with a solemn face, but then his eyes twinkled, "if not at the ends of the earth." I punched his arm and told him not to make fun of me.

Small open boats nudged up to the side of our ship as they had in Japan. We crawled down into one as our fellow travelers boarded another. Henry, careless for a moment of what anyone watching might think—we'd been told in Japan that Orientals frown on displays of affection even between family members—held my hand tightly for the entire journey from the old coaster to the rocks of the shore. We sloshed up and down through the drizzle and as we rode, secure in the knowledge that the boatman could not understand us, I told Henry my suspicions.

"Henry, dear," I whispered. "I think maybe I know the cause of my seasickness."

He turned and looked at me, silent for a change while droplets of rain beaded on his forehead. He waited for me to explain myself but, taken with a fit of shyness, I buried my face on his wet shoulder.

"Go on. What are you saying?" He shook my arm.

"We may be expecting a child."

My husband said nothing but stared straight ahead through the mist and drizzle. The corner of his mouth that I could see twitched just a bit and his eyes grew bright as stars. Then he slipped out of his new raincoat, the one I'd caught puddles in on board ship, and drew it ever so gently around me, even up over my head.

Chapter 3

One Step Forward, Two Steps Back

The moment our sampan beached after our journey through the rain from ship to shore, a crowd of shrieking, jabbering men poured down to the water's edge and began grabbing at our luggage and us. They bawled out at top voice unintelligible queries and commands at Henry and me. I couldn't comprehend what was being said to us, which made me feel like a small, none-too-bright child. My sense of humor and ability to cope deserted me as I stood in the rain at Chemulpo. Why are we doing this? I wondered. What is the point? I wanted to turn around and board that terrible ship again, if only it would take me home.

Henry must have sensed my feelings for he gripped my arm as he handed me out of the boat and onto the slippery rocks and only the dig of his fingers kept me from bolting. The shine in his eyes produced by my news about the baby changed to fierce flashes as he warned off the people who threatened to engulf us.

"Clear out!" he bellowed in newly-acquired Korean. "Get out of the way. Don't touch that!"

As soon as he could see I was safely on my feet, he waded into the brawl to deal as best he could with the shoving, shouting mob fighting over our baggage. Even though he couldn't understand much of their shrieking, he determined they should not get the best of him.

But their numbers and our poor Korean did us in at last. Henry looked at me and shrugged. "I can't do anything about this. All we can manage is to keep our baggage in sight and see where it ends up."

What a ridiculous situation. Helpless, bedraggled by the rain and apprehensive beyond words, we gave up the fight and meekly followed up the hill the gaggle of little men carrying our luggage to what turned out to be the Daibutsu Hotel.

Inside, Henry found a person who could speak English. "What must I pay?" he queried. By now I'd learned that my husband does not part easily with even his pocket change.

"Ah, sir, one small coin to each man who carried something will be fine."

"To all of them?"

"Ah, yes, sir, if you please, sir."

"Here, you do it."

The unctuous hotel manager parceled out to the noisy men the handful of coins Henry gave him, and then he showed us to a room.

As soon as we were alone, Henry began pacing up and down, rubbing his hands together. "Well, yes," he said, "this is better. A fine place. We'll be all right here." He was, to his credit, an incurable optimist. Our room was large and chilly. It did not pitch up and down like the ship so I felt better. Henry had worried about what we'd find once we landed in Korea.

"This hotel is a gift from God," he sighed. "I worried that we would be required to sleep in a native hut somewhere and eat food we could not recognize."

And I agreed with him—to a point. The large, cold room and the English-style food down in the dining room could have been much worse. But dear Henry was so tired he failed to notice we were to sleep in a shallow wooden box and that the covers were far too skimpy to keep us warm. The bed contained neither pillows nor sheets and we had to share a single washstand with all the other guests in the place.

Before we slept that night, Henry gently wrapped me in our pitiful blankets and suggested we read together from the Bible and pray before we slept.

"This is a special Sunday, you know," he said. Truth to tell, I'd forgotten it was Sunday, and I presumed he called it special because we'd arrived at last in Korea. "More even than that," he cried. "This is Easter! We came to the land of our calling on Easter Sunday." Then he pulled his diary from his pocket and read me what he'd written there: "May He who this day burst the bars of the tomb bring light and liberty to Korea."

In my bones I expected God to honor Henry's prayer. Such fervor surely amounts to something, I thought. I'd not seen much to match it through my placid, church-going childhood. How could God refuse Henry anything? So far I could not. But I didn't dwell on such lofty matters for long because my thoughts on arrival in this strange, unfamiliar place were more selfish than Henry's and certainly not on a spiritual plane.

I had never felt so sick in my life as when I was sloshing along in that terrible boat. While I focused on my illness, perhaps the Lord was relieved to see that at least one of His gospel pioneers functioned in loftier realms. Unabashed, I felt sure that He would forgive me as I got on with my task of forming a new little Appenzeller.

Two days later, Captain McGlensy of the Ossipee, the ship whose American flag so heartened us as we entered the Chemulpo harbor, called on us at our hotel.

"Rev. Appenzeller, Madam," he greeted us, a square, weather-beaten man covered in navy worsted and gold braid. "Thought I'd pay my respects, fellow Americans and all that." Something far weightier than respect-paying cropped up on his agenda even before the tea that I ordered arrived from downstairs.

"I am here in an official capacity as well," he admitted. "It is my duty to protect and defend American citizens and so I fear I must advise you not to proceed to Seoul." Seoul, Korea's capital city and our destination, lies some distance from Chemulpo, although at the time I didn't know how far. As capital it was not only the seat of government but of political activities as well.

The captain fired another salvo: "This country really is not open to missionaries and you would be beyond the protection of our flag."

From his discourse we discovered that Korea's political situation was not so settled as we were led to believe. Henry questioned the captain and argued with him although he had no solid information to reinforce his plan, just a burning desire to get on to the city and begin that which he came to do.

"Let me suggest, Rev. Appenzeller," Captain McGlensy said, after they'd batted the issue back and forth between them like a tennis ball, "that you write immediately to Lt. Foulk in Seoul. He is our U.S. charge d'affaires and can inform you as to safety of foreign life and property in the capital. If you do so, I will see that my messenger puts the letter into Lt. Foulk's hand as quickly as possible."

"Shall I do it now?"

The captain nodded. As Henry wrote his letter, McGlensy and I sipped tea and discussed his life as a naval officer and all the exotic places he visited in the line of duty. He left at last, Henry's letter in his pocket.

Late the next day Lt. Foulk's reply came. Henry read aloud his advice: "Do not come to the capital because of the extreme political situation. Proceed no further than the port city until matters here clear up."

Henry stared at the letter for a long moment, and then he let it drop to the floor as he gazed out the window at the blackness that was Chemulpo at night. Finally he spoke. "I guess that's that. We'll take up quarters in this place, then. We'll study the language, and move forward as the way opens and the Lord directs."

I stared at our pillowless box-bed realizing it was our assigned place until further notice, but as Henry pulled me into his arms I knew I'd rather be in a cold, hard place with him than in a rose garden with anyone else.

———————————

The way, however, did not open. Within two days we boarded another salty old coaster to toss and splash our way back to Japan. The reason? Almost more than I could bear.

Captain McGlensy came to see us a second time, not a pleasant visit. We received him, medals and all, in our chilly room at the Daibutsu. Henry offered him our one chair while I perched on the edge of the box-bed trying to accept the assumption that I should be as unobtrusive as possible while the men talked. The captain refused our rickety chair and paced up and down the bare floor in his gold braid and medals as if it were the deck of his ship.

"Rev. Appenzeller," he began, and a shiver of apprehension shot up my spine. I knew we would not welcome what he planned to say. He walked as he talked.

"As I told you on my last call, matters in Seoul are difficult in the extreme. Unrest and violence threaten to take over the streets. This is no time for newcomers, especially women." He shot me a glance through bushy brows as if I were an intruding barnacle to be scraped off an otherwise acceptable vessel.

"The U.S. Navy is committed to protect American interests and citizens around the world, but our commitment is difficult, if not impossible to honor when our citizens do not conduct themselves in a prudent manner. Now if you, sir," he nodded in Henry's direction as he turned on his polished black heel and headed aft, "were traveling alone without your...er, um...."

The captain had up such a head of steam by now that his good manners did not prevent him from making it crystal clear that I, the wife, was nothing but a hindrance to the commencement of Henry's missionary enterprise. He strode and snorted a while longer as he rephrased and repeated in storm-warning tones that we must not go to Seoul.

Then, adding to the inappropriateness of my presence, Captain McGlensy announced, "I cannot in good conscience risk the lives of my men for such...." Again he stumbled over his words, the gale force of his ire once more getting the best of his manners.

Henry heard the captain out and then, in a lifeless voice that cut me to the heart, said, "I understand, Captain. We will book passage on the next steamer to Japan."

After perfunctory goodbyes in my direction from both men, Henry followed the captain out of the hotel and dragged himself down to the steamship office to prepare for our departure. I stayed on the edge of the bed, more crushed in spirit than ever before in my life. I'd destroyed the dearest plans and dreams of the man I love. What could be worse? What was it about being women that caused men so much difficulty? And if we create such problems, why invite us even to supper or to church, let alone into their homes, their beds, their lives?

My mouth tasted like tarnished brass, as if I'd drunk a draught of bitter medicine—which I guess I had.

———————————

Once again we had to accept hospitality from missionaries in Japan but in a different form this time, and I was grateful for the change. A couple in Nagasaki returned home for health reasons so we used their home as our own until we could go again to Korea. Four months and some days after our marriage, Henry and I could live together in our own home. Yes, I knew it was borrowed, but I kept house and cooked for the first time since my wedding day, and I loved it.

I learned some things about life in a foreign country, although it was hard to remember that we were not in the U.S. We lived within a compound where the houses clustered inside a high wall and were nothing like the Japanese houses outside. We had green lawns, gardens, porches, even a tennis court. Most of our food was shipped from San Francisco because, the old-timers told us, Japanese products were neither adequate nor as tasty as that from home. So, being ignorant young newcomers, we ordered as they did.

A young Japanese boy helped me in the house. Because Henry and I were studying Korean rather than Japanese, I used sign language to tell him what I wanted him to do. Fortunately, he was younger than I—perhaps 18 or 19 years of age—so I would put on a stern face and played the role of housewife in charge of home and servants...well, servant.

The one dark spot on my idyll came from the fact that Henry still grieved over having to leave Korea before we even arrived, so to speak. He tried to conceal his disappointment for my sake but we both knew I was to blame. We never talked about the matter but tiptoed around it as if it were a scandal or an incurable illness. It drove a wedge between us that broke my heart. We were polite, painfully so, but the spontaneity and joy had vanished. Surely, I thought, there must be some way out of this. Will we spend the rest of our lives together like cold strangers? Why won't he talk to me about his feelings? What shall I do?

Meanwhile, Baby Appenzeller grew within me, oblivious to his part in his father's terrible pain.

Chapter 4

Almost, But Not Quite

Spring in Japan left me breathless. The beauty of April's cherry blossoms rejected my attempts at description. Some gnarled old trees with twisted trunks and reaching branches that looked like prayers stood near the entrance to the compound and often I lay in the long green grass beneath them so I could look up through the branches toward the sky. The white and pale pink flowers shimmered and shone like the live things they were, and then when blossom season passed and the petals drifted down like snow and lay around the wonderful old trees, the loveliness of it almost broke my heart because I knew it was finished for that year.

Life in that warm and sheltered place pleasured me far too much. Henry admitted to liking it, too. We lived in our own place at last, ate meals together, read borrowed books. I mended and laundered. We slept in quiet comfort, an oasis for us both as we ignored the knotted lump of feelings that lay between us. We exchanged visits with other missionaries and began to create friendships that made the prospect of leaving it all and returning to Korea something I was not eager to do.

Of course, Henry was a different story. Underneath his politeness I sensed a lost soul wandering about. He turned to letter writing to family, former parishioners, seminary classmates and friends. His letters to those friends sounded wistful at not being with them for graduation although when he made the choice to leave the U.S. before the ceremony, he was eager to get to his mission work and disdained the idea that the exercises would attract him at all.

We didn't talk at all about our feelings and thoughts, but I knew Henry was crushed by the lack of letters from his father for only one reached us in the four months since we left Lancaster. He belatedly suffered from homesickness similar to mine, but he didn't talk about it.

I pondered the strange and silent time between us. "Is this what becomes of married people?" I wondered. Henry, ever the gentleman, never rebuked me about my pregnancy or my presence although I could tell that his disappointment at being sidetracked by his wife was severe. I felt as if lead weights rode on my shoulders and that my heart had turned to stone.

Adding to our heap of unshared woes, in mid-May Will Scranton left Yokohama for Korea, leaving Loulie there under Mrs. Scranton's care. Henry spoke hardly at all on the day that news came, aside from his courteous responses to my asking, "Would you like more coffee?" and "It is growing warmer, isn't it?" He could not stand the thought that someone else would beat him to the draw, beginning missionary work in Korea while he drank tea and watched his wife's waistline disappear.

Distraction appeared just in time to push us to think about something other than ourselves. The Kitchins, long-time residents there, invited us to travel on horseback with them through rural Japan.

"Would you like to go?" Henry asked me. "What about the baby?" He laid his hand gently on my arm and I warmed to his touch, so rare amongst our miseries.

"Oh, yes, I want to. I'll be fine. I'm well and strong, I play tennis, you know, so it should be no problem at all!"

"Shall I tell them yes?" Henry's eyes kindled just a bit and I would've climbed on that horse and ridden it over a cliff to see him smile.

"Yes, darling, by all means. Let's do it."

Do it we did. After packing boxes and bags and working over maps, off we rode. Mr. and Mrs. Kitchins, a practical pair, middle-aged and wrinkled, undisturbed by fads or fashion, guided us well. They loved Japan and things Japanese so they showed us their treasures along the back roads and between the green hills. One sight from that trip will live in my mind forever. We were riding single file along a mountain trail and Mr. Kitchins had just told us a village lay ahead where we could find green tea and rest a bit.

Tink, tink, tink. A high-pitched musical sound began to creep through my thoughts about Baby Appenzeller. Tink, tink. We rounded the shoulder of a granite mountain and came upon a man with an old wooden mallet in one hand and an iron chisel in the other. He sat on the ground in the shade of a woven straw mat propped up by four poles, his clothes and hair coated with gray dust. A stone cutter. Tink, tink, tink. Steel sounded against granite.

This stone cutter was not squaring building blocks but was chiseling out, bit by bit, a god. He hammered and tapped and pounded and I knew that when he finished he would worship that which he shaped with his scarred and calloused hands. My Christian, white-clapboard-country-church upbringing came up hard against his temple-formed, multiple-god-fearing tradition and neither my mind nor my mouth would function.

I stared down from the saddle. The stone cutter knew I was there; how could he not, this pregnant foreign woman, her curly blond hair sticking out in all directions from under her hat. But he ignored me. Tink, tink, tink. The stone chips showered about him as he worked on the face of his image, shaping eyes and a high, bulging forehead out of stone.

A gap yawned between us two human beings. I wondered if he rummaged among his beliefs, or lack thereof, as I was doing when confronted with the unknown. Even brought up, as I was, with teachings about the Creator God (no-other-gods-before-me), I found my brain shut down before the fact that others elsewhere—represented by this dust-covered workman—had not sat in little Sunday school chairs and learned to sing "Jesus Loves Me."

What did he learn to sing? Why is there a difference between him and me? Did it matter?

God? gods? What's the difference, he might say to me. We are Japanese. We worship in the temple in the village. So did my parents, my grandparents, all my ancestors back to the beginning of time. My father cut stone, I cut stone, and my son when he returns from school will join me here and I will teach him how to cut stone.

Mildly shocked by the direction (or lack thereof) of my thinking, I searched around within my own mind and heart for a guiding star, a signpost, something that would answer my heretical questions, that would tell me what to think, how to feel about the man and his task at which I stared. What my attitude should be.

But on my side of the gap, the chasm, that separated us, I felt nothing.

I shook the reins and my horse began to move again along the trail. The stone cutter glanced at me and we both, in the accepted Japanese form, bowed courteously. I rode on around the mountain while tink, tink, tink reverberated in my head.

———■———

"Ella, look! A letter!"

"Oh, Henry, I told you your father would write soon. Let me see."

"No, no, this is from Will Scranton, from Korea!"

I didn't care if it had come from the North Pole so long as it had my husband smiling again. "Read it," I ordered.

"Will says Korea's political feuds are easing up and we can go back."

I told myself I was pleased to be off at last although I couldn't help gazing back over my shoulder at the first home Henry and I had ever known together.

We sailed June 16: Henry and I, Loulie and Mrs. Scranton plus new recruits, the Herons. I loved being reunited with Loulie—she'd been in Yokohama, I in Nagasaki—and I managed, in the main, to stay clear of Mrs. Scranton. When we landed in Chemulpo on the 21st, sunshine burst through Henry's clouds at last and he began to feel once again like a missionary to Korea.

Will Scranton met Loulie, his mother and the Herons (another doctor newly arriving in Korea) and took them to Seoul straightaway. He planned that both families would lodge with Dr. and Mrs. Horace

Allen (all those medical people did hang together) at the U.S. Legation. The Allens had gone to Korea as missionaries like us, but politics and royal distrust had caused the Korean king to forbid them from promoting Christian teachings among the Korean people. Allen had already established himself, however, with the American government and enjoyed great respect and privilege from that quarter. Thus Horace Allen, MD, was appointed to man the U.S. Legation in Seoul. From this vantage point, we were told, he was encouraged by the king to practice Western-style medicine in the capital, even with the royal family.

"Come with us, Henry," Will urged. "You are welcome at the Allens, too." And the Herons and the Scrantons and the Allens? All in one house? I balked.

"Henry," I tugged his sleeve as he chattered away. "Henry? Listen to me a minute." He stopped at last and looked down at me, a frown creasing his forehead.

"We can't go there," I whispered in his ear.

"Why ever not? They invited us."

"Henry, that means four families in one house! Where would we sleep? On the roof?"

He stared at me for a moment, then nodded slowly, frown still in place. I felt so relieved when he said to Will, "Ah...would you please express our thanks to the Allens? My wife and I are weary from the crossing and feel we should stay here until she...we...recover."

"And also," he went on, surprising me, "we will find temporary lodging here until I can locate a permanent home for us in Seoul."

Everything he said about our needing recovery was true. The sea again had turned mean on our crossing and some of us could neither eat nor drink until the waves calmed down, which they finally did the last couple of days at sea. When we disembarked once again in Chemulpo, I vowed never to set foot in another fusty, rusty steamship.

What a silly thing to say. What else does a missionary do but sail about in ships?

The Fourth of July, America's beloved holiday, came upon Henry and me as we waited in our little Korean house in Chemulpo. On the very night we arrived, soon after we parted from the others, we contracted for that small boards-and-mud place. Henry liked it, however, for it cost only $25 per month. It was not what you'd call nice but it served, and we knew we'd acquire something better in Seoul before winter.

On the Fourth we were, of course, alone together. Mid-morning, Henry closed his books and laid aside his pen and paper. We climbed the hill that overlooks the harbor for we hoped that a ship from the United States might be lying at anchor and we could see the Stars and Stripes, but none was there. Oh, well. We ate a small picnic in the grass at the top of the hill anyway and felt the sea breeze blow against our faces.

Just a few days later *chang-ma*, Korean rainy season, broke over our heads. Literally. Rain water passed through our little house unhindered by such a thing as a waterproof roof. We dashed about with pans and buckets to catch the drips and pours. Each room leaked and few places existed where we could sit or stand out of the wet. Henry plodded on with his projects; however, sitting at the rickety table with sheets of paper spread out about him.

"What is that?" I asked. "What are you doing?"

"Forming plans."

Just as we spoke, the drip-drip-drip of rain into the pan at his elbow turned into a steady pour like lemonade from a pitcher. Its force overwhelmed the pan and water splattered out on all sides. Before he could move them, Henry's neat outlines turned to blotches of blue ink, and then the blotches swelled into rivulets that ran off the edge of the table and splashed to the floor.

Henry looked so nonplussed and helpless as he picked at the corners of the sodden sheets, watching his plans disappear into the deluge. I think I snickered because he turned on me, almost angry.

"Did you laugh?" he rumbled.

I shrugged and gestured helplessly at his papers, amused by our ridiculous dilemma.

"What's so funny?"

"Well, do admit..." I began before I lost control. I threw my head back and laughed so hard I couldn't stop. Henry glared for a moment longer and then seemed to understand. There we were, two sodden people paying $25 a month to live in a wooden sieve set on a Korean hill where rain came down in torrents. Our papers, clothes, floors, furniture—all wet, wet, wet.

Henry jumped up from his chair, scooped up his soaked papers and wrung them out like a rag between his big square hands. Then he dropped them into the overflowing pan on the table.

"So much for those plans."

By now he was laughing, too. A little. "Not such good ones anyway. I'll begin again when the sun shines."

We assumed it would shine again even though it was difficult to maintain that assumption when the rain poured down on us day after day after day. At that moment, however, I learned that laughter beats crying any day, whatever the mess I found myself in.

And believe me, in Korea, a multitude of messes awaited us.

Chapter 5

South Gate Welcome

Late in July on a day when the rains held back although the clouds looked as round and ready to deliver as I felt, we left our shabby little Chemulpo house and set out for Seoul. Word had come from the legation in Seoul that the political mood had settled down somewhat and we should come. Riding rented horses and followed by a retinue of baggage-bearing ponies, we wound through valleys carpeted with emerald green rice paddies. People worked knee-deep in mud amongst the half-grown plants and as we trudged along the narrow paths, they raised up to stare at our caravan. Our foreignness gave them something to talk about, I'm sure, and perhaps a moment's easement for their aching backs. Henry, riding ahead of me, kept shouting back over his shoulder, remarking on all he saw.

"Ella, look! Babies on their backs." He pointed to women bent over their work, some of whom wore a swaddled bundle between shoulder blades and waist.

"Yes, and look here, under this tree. Here's one asleep on the grass." Babies interested us in those days, as did all the differences we discovered in Korea.

We reached Seoul at sundown. Henry grew quiet as we rode into the city. I felt sure he was at prayer, but while he prayed I gaped at the towering gate through which we passed, one of the loveliest and most unusual buildings I had ever seen.

Eight gates punctuated Seoul's wall, not gates as I think of them, little white picket things with hollyhocks, but tall, broad structures big as two-story farm houses. The four main gates matched the points of the compass and we entered the capital through South Gate just at sundown. Men in red and blue uniforms wearing round black hats were heaving on the heavy wooden doors, preparing to close and bolt them for the night. Our pony drivers shouted at them to wait for us; otherwise we would have had to camp outside the wall overnight.

I stared up at South Gate, fascinated by its double roof, tiled and with tip-tilted corners. On each up-curved point sat seven little carved creatures, something like long-tailed monkeys or mysterious birds, silhouetted against the evening sky. Up under the eaves the carved ends of the beams were painted with bright colors: red, blue, green and yellow.

Huge squared stones formed the body of the gate and on these the wooden roof structures rested. The entrance itself consisted of two thick, narrow wooden doors with rounded tops. A heavy bolt dropped across the doors to bar them shut at night.

Will Scranton walked out to South Gate to meet us and as we stood chattering with excitement, we heard and felt a deep mellow reverberation foreign to anything we had ever experienced before.

"What was that?" Henry asked him.

"Each evening the great bell is struck," Will replied, "and as it rings all city gates are closed until morning."

"What sort of bell makes such a deep-throated sound?"

Will chuckled. "The biggest bell you've ever seen. And to top it off, it has no clapper."

"But how..."

"Never mind now," Will waved us back to our mounts. "I'll show you the bell tomorrow. Let's go home now. Loulie's waiting."

Off we rode, shut in for the night in the city that was to be our home. Will it ever seem less strange, more like home? I wondered. I did like South Gate, however, and knew I would go back to it again and again.

———————————————

Loulie set up cots for us in Dr. Scranton's apothecary, his "tablet house," they called it.

"Here we will stay," I grumbled as we dragged our baggage into what looked to me like a chicken coop, "until we can find a place of our own, a project we've pursued ever since our marriage last December."

My thoughts turned dreary and so did my comments. My emotional state was not a pleasant one as I looked around for a place to sit down.

"Guess the side of the bed will have to do," I decided, "because pills and baggage monopolize the rest of the space." In the Scranton house it wasn't so bad. Loulie and Mrs. Scranton awaited us with lamps lit and a meal spread. Loulie and I squealed and hugged each other hard. Her warm welcome and their hospitality meant so much after our long day in the saddle and the bombarding of our senses with so much that was strange and different. Right after dinner, Henry and I begged off from parlor chit-chat and returned to our cots in the tablet house.

"Ah, Ella, did you ever see such a place?"

"No, I've never seen so much medicine in my entire life."

"No, girl! I don't mean that. I mean this country...all that we saw today as we rode along."

What did we see? Thatch-roofed houses that from a distance looked charming and picturesque, like mushrooms cuddled down at the base of a hill. But up close, filth and dilapidation. Small children playing in the dirt dressed as miniature versions of their parents and whose hair had not been washed since God alone knows when.

Women beating their laundry on rocks beside puddles and streams who stopped to stare and stare again as our entourage slowly wound through their world. Farmers lounging on the dikes between their flourishing rice fields while their bony oxen grazed nearby. I took a talking fit and was telling Henry all this when he interrupted.

"And what about the tiled roofs of the wealthy homes? Those people are called '*yangban*,' and they never dirty their hands with common toil. They live off their tenants!"

Determined to have my say, I countered with, "Well, what about those old stone turtles with the pillars on their backs? Those are tributes to ancestors...and..."

Always quicker and louder, Henry seized the lead. "Devil posts, the pony drivers called them, those tall carved things at the edges of the villages with the hideous faces. They're supposed to protect the villagers from evil."

Neither one of us had enough energy to keep talking so we embraced in the space between our cots, shared a long kiss—which was lots more pleasant than both trying to talk at the same time—blew out the candle and fell into bed. Henry was snoring before I got my nightgown tucked down around my feet.

Despite stubbing my toes against the clutter in the Scranton tablet house, I loved being near Loulie once again. We drank gallons of tea and never tired of talking together, especially when Mrs. Scranton was occupied elsewhere. That woman always made me feel as if I should stand at attention when addressing her. Loulie shriveled too whenever her mother-in-law was in the same room. One day we talked about our feelings and Loulie told me a story.

"While we still lived in Cleveland, Will fell ill, terribly ill. I worked as hard as I could to care for him but he didn't improve. One day his mother appeared on our doorstep.

"'I've come to care for William,' she announced. 'You may prepare a bed for me in the sickroom.'

"Mother Scranton moved into his room, shut the door and assumed all responsibility for *my* husband's care. She allowed me only to prepare meal trays for them both and do the laundry."

She paused and stared down at her hands, tears collecting on her eyelashes. "Will got well, obviously, so I guess I should be thankful to his mother and not dwell on my own feelings about it all."

I said nothing when she finished—what *could* I say?—but I threw my arms around her and we both cried a little. I drew comfort from knowing that I am not alone in my dread of the formidable Mrs. Scranton.

Talking with Loulie about my condition—why did we call it that? What's wrong with "pregnancy"?—comforted me. She already had a little girl and so when I confessed to being sleepy all the time, to craving unavailable fruit, she understood. I didn't lack time to nap because there was little else for me to do. Henry and Will prowled the city looking at property. I couldn't unpack when we had no house, so Loulie and I drank tea and talked.

Henry and I did walk out a little within our neighborhood, but we had to be careful; foreigners were still unwelcome. On these excursions I looked at people as carefully as I could without intruding, although they didn't offer us the same courtesy. They stared at us without remorse, often with half open mouths, mesmerized by our foreignness. We knew we offered an uncommon sight to the average Korean: big noses, strangely colored hair, outlandish clothes and eyes that looked to them like bits of broken blue glass.

"You know, Henry," I said as we strolled along the palace wall near the Scrantons' house, "before I left America I thought all Orientals were yellow-skinned. But looking at Koreans I see all kinds of skin colors, none of them yellow. "Farmers are leathery brown from the sun, just like Americans. Here in Seoul some look, um...maybe ivory-colored, all smooth and even. Others have ruddy cheeks and skin as white as mine."

Henry nodded, his head tilted to one side as he listened to me. For once he didn't seize control of the conversation, so I went on. "The longer I look at them, the more variety I see...and this nips off at the roots the impression I grew up with about people from this side of the world."

"I'm having similar feelings," he said. "We've a lot to learn."

One afternoon a few days later I was dozing on my cot through the heat of the afternoon when Henry dashed into our room bursting with joy and good spirits.

"I've found it!"

"What had you lost, dear?"

"No, no, I didn't lose anything. I found our property! Where we can live!" He had my full, wide-awake attention.

"Where, Henry? Tell me quick."

"Just next door to this," he gestured at the Scranton buildings, "land is for sale. We begin negotiations tomorrow and I'm sure the Lord will give it to us, and for a decent price, too."

"Is there a house?"

"Yes, there's a wonderful old *yangban*'s house that I am sure we can repair and make into a perfect home for us. I can't take you to see it until negotiations are well under way because we daren't exhibit too much enthusiasm."

"What is a *yangban*?"

"A Korean nobleman."

"Why not express enthusiasm?"

"It would drive the price up, I'm told. We must remain calm and at least semi-disinterested. It helps our bargaining position." At that he loped off in search of Will Scranton, neither calm nor disinterested. How will he fare in the bargaining process? I wondered.

Meanwhile, I sent a $100 food order to San Francisco. Huge sum. We found little in South Gate market we could eat—or so we thought at the time—except tough beef, chickens and eggs. Steamers do not cross the Pacific in the winter so we felt we should lay in supplies enough to last until spring.

Then Henry told me he did it. He managed to buy the adjoining property for the mission and we could finally expect to have a home of our own. And to ice the cake, I should be just across the lawn from Loulie...when we had a lawn. What could be finer?

———※———

Mail for the Herons, the Scrantons and the Appenzellers came to the American Legation situated just over the wall from the Scrantons and Herons. On days when a ship was due, all of us dithered with excitement, knowing we would hear from home.

With one exception. Father Appenzeller refused to write his son, a heavy burden for Henry to bear. His silence stemmed from his disapproval of Henry's choice of careers. He didn't want his handsome son to waste himself on Koreans, feeling Henry should be at home in Pennsylvania farming, in business, or pastoring a church.

Mother Appenzeller also opposed our going. She wrote letters, but filled them with tales of her nightmares that Henry would drown someday on the wrong side of the world. As I read her missives I often wished she'd be the silent one. Her morbid fears gave me the shivers. Henry could not talk about these problems, his pain was so great. He wrote several times protesting Father Appenzeller's failure to communicate but without response.

We tried, meanwhile, to learn to communicate in Korean using, of all things, a French-Korean dictionary that slowed us down to snail speed. Henry chatted in the markets and along the streets with anyone who would let him practice. He didn't mind if people laughed. Which I did, too, when I overheard a remarkable conversation among my husband, his language teacher and the teacher's friend who used some English.

"How long will you be in our country?" asked the teacher's friend.

"We hope to stay for a good long while," Henry replied.

"Why are you here?"

"Well, we want to learn to speak Korean and we also would like to teach English and other subjects here." Henry knew he shouldn't talk about religion although his desire to share his faith burned in his heart like a furnace. Such talk was banned by the king.

"Thank you for coming." Even though I couldn't see them, I imagined his polite bow at this point. "I think I know a way I can make your time with us more pleasant and comfortable."

"Oh, really? How is that?" Henry sounded interested.

"I know a fine woman, strong and healthy and submissive, that you can have for $100...."

At that point I slipped away out of earshot. I knew what Henry would say about the man's offer of a second wife—so they're called in Korean, we'd say "mistress"—although I didn't know at what volume he would give it. Also, although I clamped my handkerchief tightly over my mouth I feared they might hear me snicker and the visitors would find out that Henry's first wife was disrespectful and not at all submissive.

Late in August just at sundown Henry led me through a gap in the Scranton wall to see the property he intended to buy for our home and his school, for despite the edict against propagating Christianity, Korea wanted Western education along with Dr. Allen's medicine.

"Ella, you draw so well. Would you sketch a map of this property and the location of the buildings? I need to send it to the home office."

Who could resist those glowing eyes and that square chin? "Of course, darling. I'll do it for you. Let's look at it all, every stick and stone."

We stayed until dark, exploring and sketching. It was lovely to wander about among the buildings and up the hill behind, dreaming of how we would make it all into a home.

The house, a *yangban*'s or nobleman's home, folded itself around a central courtyard and every room opened onto the court with sliding wood and paper doors. Beside the large square main house— ours was a touch larger than the Scrantons—a tangle of outbuildings intended for storage, stables and servant quarters made up the rest of the facilities. We discussed which would survive and which we would remove to make space for more useful purposes.

Because we and the Scrantons and Herons lived just over the wall from the American Legation, eventually we all carved out a little United States there in Seoul just as the missionaries had in Japan. Comfortable and secure and close to each other, we worked to make our space resemble our familiar homeland as much as possible.

Henry wrote his first report to Rev. Maclay in Japan and sent it with my sketch of the property. He also told about the four students who met with him for "Western learning," the reason the King was given for our presence in his country. He also mentioned that Will Scranton was seeing patients in his little clinic.

I don't think he told him that Will and Dr. Allen parted company professionally after a few short weeks of working together in the government hospital. "Big trouble," Loulie told me had come up between them but she didn't elaborate because she'd heard Mrs.

Scranton marching down the hall toward us. I would learn more of this in days to come.

———————■———————

Early in September I acquired a new problem to ponder. Loulie's little girl took sick and Loulie was beside herself with worry. Will looked in on her, but only occasionally.

"How can he do this?" I railed at Henry amongst the pills. "His own baby is burning up with fever and he spends all day seeing Koreans! What's wrong with him?"

"He's doing the Lord's work," Henry defended, but I could see questions in his eyes. "After all, that's what we came here for and to do so requires sacrifice sometimes."

"But what about his baby? And his wife? Doesn't the Lord want him to take care of them, and shouldn't he do that first?"

We reached no solution to the problem and questions whirled round in my head for days. Is this what is expected of missionaries? Must we always set aside personal needs for God's work? If the baby should die, how can Loulie bear it? How can Will? He may have the skill to save her, but he's so busy saving others, which is why he went to Korea in the first place. What is right? How does one choose?

———————■———————

"Let's walk over and see how much they did today." Every evening after dinner, Henry tugged me through the fence to see with him the progress on our house.

"Only four rooms for now. Winter's coming, you know." Four rooms sounded palatial to us, especially because we knew they'd be free of Will Scranton's pills and we could sleep in our double bed instead of on two cots. In mid-September on one of our inspection tours, I decided to speak to Henry about the trouble we'd ignored for months, even though the tension between us was almost gone. I plunged into the middle of it.

"Henry, have you forgiven me?"

He stopped pulling at a window frame and looked down at me. "What did you say?"

"Have you forgiven me?"

"For what?"

"For causing you so much heartbreak back in Chemulpo when we had to return to Japan. Oh, darling, I felt terrible when that awful Captain McGlensy made it so obvious it was my fault you couldn't go on to Seoul. I knew you were crushed by disappointment...and we couldn't ever talk about it...even in Japan...and oh, it hurt so much...."

By then I was sobbing and choking on my words. Henry sat down on the edge of the little wooden porch that is part of every Korean home. He pulled me onto his lap, wrapped his strong arms around me and let me weep in his shirt collar.

"Ella, dear Ella," he whispered. "Don't cry. It's all right. Of course I forgive you."

Then he gently pushed me back so we could look at each other. "It is hard to talk about some things, the deep things, the painful things," he said. He dropped his eyes and struggled to drag the reluctant words to the surface.

"I did blame you for a time, and for this I'm truly sorry. I am the one who needs forgiveness."

"Oh, Henry, don't...."

"No, no, let me finish. You and I both know that my instructions said I should enter Korea first and then send for you when the time was right. I ignored this because I couldn't bear the thought of separating from you for so long. I love you so, Ella, and having found such happiness and contentment with you, I refused to forego these joys at the direction of some old man half a world away."

"Oh, Henry" was all I could think of to say as I threw my arms around his neck, this time in shining joy, tears forgotten.

"Let's forgive each other, and promise never, never to leave unsaid between us the things we need to talk about, no matter how distressing."

"You ask a great deal," my husband replied, "from a dour, unemotional Pennsylvania Dutchman...but yes, we should try. We must never again allow misunderstanding to grow up between us. If talking is required, then we'll talk!"

My joy and contentment bloomed at that moment beyond anything I dreamed possible. Baby Appenzeller seemed to sense my happiness as he joined the celebration by leaping and kicking in my middle. Suddenly it came to me—we were more than newlywed missionaries. We were almost a family. That corner of the porch, where Henry declared he couldn't bear for us to be apart, became almost sacred to me, one of the most precious places in our home.

Chapter 6

Tears, Tantrums, and Triumphs

We bought a cow, with calf, for $10.50. Henry didn't even wince over the outlay, probably because I promised to make butter. Loulie helped me buy a jar in South Gate Market shaped just like Mother's churn and Henry carved a dasher to fit it. I collected the cream that rose on the milk from our new cow and made butter, realizing as I puttered in Loulie's kitchen that I was copying my mother exactly. What a fit of homesickness that produced. "She taught me so much," I fretted. "When will I ever see her dear face again?"

My parents were already old. Would they live until our furlough year? Were they heartbroken because this grandchild of theirs would be born so far away? They would never see our baby's early smiles or first steps, nor hear him learn to talk or feel the touch of his tiny hands. They would be strangers to him and he to them. Such thoughts pained my very bones. I felt like stamping my foot at God and telling Him his price was too high, more than I could pay.

Henry found me dripping tears into the milk, which wasn't even spilled. He didn't scold, however, when I told him what was the matter. He just held me close, as best he could with the baby intruding between us. Grappling as he was with the problem of his parents' disapproval, in those days he knew how to comfort me.

After mopping up my tears, Henry suggested we go and look at our house. Between our place and the Scrantons' about 60 men pounded, sawed, dug, lifted and carried. One particular maneuver tickled his funny bone.

"Come and see the Korean steam shovel."

We walked around behind the house and he pointed at three men working. One held the long handle of a shovel while two others pulled on ropes tied low on the handle. These three, however, operating one shovel between them, did not move more dirt nor do it faster than one workman does with a similar shovel back home. It took three men to move a shovelful of dirt! We both chuckled, always a good thing.

We poked our heads into the house to see how work progressed. "Well, praise the Lord!" Henry looked at me curiously, startled by my sudden spiritual joy.

"The smell," I told him. "It's gone." The house was two or three centuries old and had not been properly cleaned for at least one of them. But clean paper, whitewash, newly oiled beams and considerable scrubbing freshened the scent as well as the sight of our new home and I was pleased and relieved.

During those early months in Korea, Henry had much more contact with Korean people than I did. Part of the blame for that lay on my pregnancy and part on the pressures of the culture, plus that was just the way we foreigners functioned in those days. Henry would sometimes come home fuming at the way Koreans did things. Other times he grew lyrical about their many sterling qualities. As he drifted back and forth in his opinions about the country and its people, his changeability seemed faithless and wrong to me, but I thought I understood.

He found Korean men appealing because of their height, their erect bearing, their physical grace. He called them "large and robust and well-developed." He loved to watch men move through Seoul streets in their flowing white garments topped by wide-brimmed horsehair hats tied snugly over their long hair, which was twisted up in a topknot. Henry was less enthusiastic about their smoking habits, frowning over the long thin pipe that accompanied them everywhere.

On the other hand, Henry insisted, "The Korean man is the laziest individual I ever encountered." He showed me a letter in which he aired his opinions. "All Korea seems to be run on the poet's principle; man wants but little here below. The average workman is indifferent about work. If it does not suit him, he will walk off."

Harsh words. I bit back my arguments because after all, he handled the workmen; I did not. "They're happy to do what I ask them," he fussed, "but they want to do it tomorrow. The only thing they prefer doing today is smoke and drink 'sool'...that's barley wine."

Henry troubled me when he talked about problems he perceived in Korean character because he ranted on and on, faster and harder, with his negative comments until the positive side of the matter vanished in the avalanche of his displeasure. This side of my husband I'd never seen before.

"Is it all too much?" I mused. "Too much newness? No home to hide in? Inability to talk Korean beyond surface chit-chat?" Until then I thought of Henry as the eternal optimist, but no more.

———◆———

The calf died, a grave loss but better than losing his mother. We and the Scrantons enjoyed the butter and milk and would've felt that absence much more keenly.

The worst part of the calf's death, however, was what happened to its carcass. Henry paid two coolies to haul it out of the city but then came stomping into our pill-packed guest room, ignoring my shushing and fussing and ranting at top voice over the fate of the poor calf.

"It is incredible! Unbelievable!"

"What, dear?"

"You will never believe what I just found out...they ate it! They cut it up and ate it! That calf died of who-knows-what ailment and those men took my money to carry it home to their families and feast on it!" The veins in Henry's neck bulged like tow ropes on the Erie Canal.

"Well, what happened? Are they ill?" I imagined homes full of dead and dying people stricken by bad meat acquired from the foreigners.

"Oh, no, they're fine. Nothing happened. It's a miracle. So much for Western science and medical expertise."

Henry shrugged his shoulders and mumbled to himself as he paced up and down our room, his color subsiding from red to pale pink. We both pondered what might have happened but didn't. What if the coolies, in eating the dead animal, had succumbed to some dreadful disease? What would that have done to our acceptance in Korea? Had we experienced a moment of divine protection in a matter that could've been fatal to our purposes in going to that upside-down place? We knew little about crises at that point but we learned plenty before we were through.

In mid-October we moved at last into our beautiful home. No more tossing ship's cabin, no more missionary guest rooms, no more tablet house. Just our own four rooms with the promise of more when time and funds permitted.

The bedroom was my favorite. I could lie in bed and look up at the wood rafters and beams which, while holding up the roof, also beautified the interior in a uniquely Korean way. The rafters, 48 of them, ran up to a peak in the center. They were intersected once by a heavy wooden crossbeam, and then at the peak they all met at another beam. Workmen oiled all this wood, staining it dark as walnut. Between the rafters and on the walls the workmen applied pure white rice paper. The contrast of dark and light between wood and paper drew my eyes and calmed my soul. We covered the floors with straw matting and over this we spread in the living room the blue and gray carpet we brought from the United States. The walnut bedroom set with the dresser's marble top looked so comfortable and homey, especially after we unpacked lamps and mirrors and pictures plus a clock. On the bed I spread the white Marseille counterpane and pillow shams I embroidered myself.

Completing the comforts of that room, a rocking chair stood near the dresser and a wood stove waited in the corner. Henry insisted on hanging pictures so family photos smiled at us from the walls.

I couldn't persuade myself to put out my cut glass perfume bottles just yet nor the tatted doilies Mother made for us. What if they were smashed or stained? My most precious things stayed packed away.

Because of the Korean-style sliding doors that served as walls, we could arrange rooms as we pleased. We created a dining-sitting room, a study and a kitchen along with the bedroom. I felt again as I did in Japan when we enjoyed living in our borrowed house for it pleased me to be able to arrange furniture and decorations, making our rooms homey and bright.

Loulie popped in one evening just as Henry finished hanging the pictures. She rapped on the door, then pulled it aside and called out in Korean, "Is anybody home?"

"Please come in," Henry responded, using his best language skills.

"Oh, Loulie, come and see," I squealed, using my best English. I showed her around all four rooms, babbling on about the treasures we'd unpacked and the repairs that had finally been completed.

She tapped her slippered foot—we took shoes off at the door, a Korean custom—on the blue carpet. "A rug? Where did you get this?" Her eyes turned cold.

"We brought it from America."

"What a good idea. We never thought about doing that. And lamps to match. It looks wonderful in here." Such nice words. Why did they feel more like an indictment than a compliment?

Loulie stared at the lamps on the dresser, which had blue cabbage roses painted on their shades. Then she spoke again and the chill in the air matched her eyes. "How lucky you are that your husband can take so much time to work on your house. A man's strength and skills make such a difference."

I tried for our old warmth. "Yes, I'm so grateful. With our baby due so soon, I'm worthless for furniture pushing or ladder climbing."

Loulie's eyes flicked about the room. I could tell she liked it but something was wrong. "Well, my Will is so busy every day, all day long, with patients that he scarcely takes time to breathe, let alone play around the house with his family. We're just so thankful for the Christian influence he's having already on these poor people, so I guess we can make do with a less-than-elegant home...but don't misunderstand, I'm happy for you, Ella. It's obvious this is all very important to you, so I'm glad you have it...."

With that she dashed to the door. She slid into her shoes and bolted off the little porch before I could maneuver my bulk to follow her. I peered out into the dark but she'd disappeared.

"What's wrong?" My insides twisted with unanswered questions. "I don't know what to do. What shall I say? Have I lost my friend?"

Chapter 7

To See the King

Alice Rebecca arrived November 9th. Both Henry and I were besotted by our first precious child. When Henry sat in the rocking chair by the warm stove with Alice in his arms I loved to gaze at the two of them. That picture of father and baby daughter still glows in my mind.

On the afternoon of Alice's birth day I began to feel strange, not in pain exactly but aware that my back and abdominal muscles were squeezing and contracting in an unfamiliar way, making me wonder if my time had come. I slid open the study door where Henry was teaching English to several boys. Thanks to edicts from the palace, he could not evangelize, but the king was interested in Korean boys receiving western-style educations, so, lacking a proper school as yet, Henry had begun his teaching in the simplest way possible. In his personal study with a circle of curious boys.

"Could I see you for a moment, dear?" I thought I murmured calmly but he glanced up with a frown...and then froze. I must have looked awful because he jumped to his feet, overturning his chair and startling his students right out of their manners. As they swiveled to see what was amiss I shrank from the door, unwilling for them to see my distended silhouette. Henry recovered his wits enough to dismiss them...sort of. I could hear him through the paper door.

"Oh, uh...our lesson is finished for today." He said it twice, once in English and once in stuttering Korean. He then began gathering up papers, pens and books, thrusting them into the boys' hands oblivious to their bewildered faces and muttered questions.

"What's this? What's the trouble?"

"Is Teacher ill?"

"Maybe's it's Teacher's honorable wife...."

"So strange...."

Shaking their heads and hissing through their teeth, the boys shuffled into their shoes and departed. Henry jerked back the bedroom door and gripped my arms. "Ella! What? Is it time? What's happening?" He began to shake me like a naughty child and when I protested he dropped into a puddle of remorse.

"Oh, I'm so sorry. I don't know what to do. Forgive me, did I hurt you?"

"Tell Will Scranton that Baby Appenzeller is on the way. I don't feel so well." By this time the squeezing sensation was accompanied by aches that meant business even to my inexperienced thinking.

"You go," I told Henry, "and let him know, then come right back to me."

He turned without a word, jerked open the outside door, leapt off the little porch and dashed across the yard to the Scranton house hatless, coatless and oblivious to the fact that he still wore his house slippers. I started to chuckle at the sight when a massive pain cut off my laughter and left me gasping. I dropped onto a straight chair and sat there wondering what to do next when Loulie came running up to the house.

"Ella? Ella?" she called. "I'm coming. Don't worry. I'm coming."

In she rushed, forgetting to remove her shoes—I saw everything so clearly at a time when I expected total befuddlement—and drawing me up off the chair, started to unbutton my dress. "It's time," she crooned, "time for Baby Appenzeller to come to this house, it's time, it's time...."

Her gentle voice and gentler hands comforted and encouraged me as she slipped me out of my clothes and into a nightgown. Just as she turned back the bed covers another pain hit. "I know," she said as I doubled over in agony. "It's awful, isn't it? But just a little while and it will be over; just a little while and he'll be here."

The sound of her soft singsong plus her loving, touching, helping hands calmed me and made me feel safe. The pain ebbed and I smiled my thanks at my friend.

"I'll tell the cook to boil water. I'll only be a minute."

When Loulie came back from the kitchen she said, "Dr. Scranton is setting a broken leg. He'll be here soon. There isn't much to do at the beginning but wait for the baby to make his journey, so I came first."

I clutched her hand. "I'm so glad," I began, but another pain swept my words away and although I gritted my teeth hard to prevent any noise, I think I groaned or wailed.

So it went. Will Scranton arrived in time and in spite of pain and mess, it pleasures me to remember Alice's birth. And Henry always bragged that his baby was the first Western child born in Korea.

———————◼———————

Korea still was not a comfortable place for foreigners like us and not because of the lack of food and accommodations we were accustomed to. The political pot boiled incessantly. Rumors of impending riots ran through Seoul streets like water during rainy season. Gossip whispered that China or Japan planned to attack. Tales of the butchery of traitors sent shivers crawling up my spine, especially when we learned that those tales were true. Henry discovered that two men implicated in the post office horror last year, the incident that delayed our arrival in Korea, were captured, beheaded and their corpses displayed near South Gate for three days. Atrocities, it seemed, were part of life in Seoul.

As I nursed my baby near the stove I couldn't help wondering how such heinous behavior would affect us. How might we react to such sights? Would the turmoil drive us out? How very far we were from the safe green hills of Pennsylvania.

The uproar related to the struggle between conservative Koreans entrenched in high places versus liberals who longed for change and modernization, a struggle between China (conservative) and Japan (progressive), both of whom wanted to sink their colonialistic claws into the Korean peninsula. The uprising and assassination attempts at the new post office before our arrival lurked in people's minds and they feared reprisals because high officials and even the royal family were involved.

I didn't understand it then and due to my confinement I didn't see many people, but I sensed thick tension in the air. It reminded me of bitter cold days at home when wires strung along the roadsides hummed and whined like a toothache. Horace Underwood, fellow missionary and our traveling companion between Japan and Korea, came often in the evening to meet with Henry and they discussed Korean politics into the night. I served them tea and then retired to the bedroom and Alice, usually too sleepy to be sociable. I could hear the rumble of their voices, however, through the paper door and I knew what they were talking about.

Horace and Henry had become good friends. It began by the two of them comparing notes on language study. From that blossomed their mutual dream to translate the Bible into Korean. They began that work by transliterating the New Testament's proper names into Korean. This beginning step in their monumental task was possible because written Korean uses an excellent phonetic alphabet. To us who depended on the ABCs to communicate, the Korean alphabet looked at first like a hodge-podge collection of circles, right and left angles and little curved tails. But we discovered that the system was easy to learn and, better yet, each symbol could be trusted to sound the same whenever it appeared, with very few exceptions.

I knew about all their lofty intentions but to me the best part of Horace and Henry's friendship was seeing and hearing them together. Something special took place. An electricity of sorts crackled in the air when they discussed issues and ideas. They respected and enjoyed each other as equals in intelligence and commitment.

The sight of them together amused me. Henry was tall and articulate with gentle eyes (until something angered him). Horace was shorter and bristled with energy. Even his hair wanted to stand on end and he used slathers of pomade to control it. When he spoke he convinced us that he knew all the answers by delivering them in a loud, authoritative voice that permitted no dissension. Henry may have been the only person in our little foreign community who ever dared disagree with Horace and they did get into an occasional shouting match, which made me smile for they sounded like two boys arguing over a game of marbles.

———————————

Our first Christmas in Korea was both sweet and sad. Alice blessed our home with joy and we talked of how Joseph and Mary must have felt about the arrival of Jesus in a hostile city far from home.

"Politics had that country in an uproar, too, what with Roman occupation and taxes," Henry said, "which is why Mary bore her son in a strange town. They had to be counted in a census, which would lead to more taxes."

"She didn't even have an ancient Korean house to shelter her nor a wood stove to keep her warm," I said. "They were aliens like us and trying like everything to find a safe place to be."

Henry and I both, unbeknownst to each other, had squirreled away a couple of small gifts for the holiday. I gave him two linen handkerchiefs and a bottle of bay rum, which I'd hidden in the bottom of one of our trunks. He found two brass candlesticks in South Gate Market that almost matched and that I kept on the dining table ever afterwards. We both gave Alice all the love and warmth we were capable of.

Mid-afternoon on the 25th the three of us went across to the Scranton house where Loulie and Mrs. Scranton prepared dinner for us, the Herons and Horace Underwood. We ate it with pleasure, glad not to be alone.

We each felt an emptiness, I know, at being so far from loved ones back home. Neither Henry nor I had ever spent that dearest of holidays outside our family circles before and to do so in a place ignorant of Christ's birth where just over the compound wall life and commerce continued as on every other day felt sad, incomplete, and in spite of all our efforts, infinitely lonely.

After dinner Henry put his arm around my shoulders and said, "Let's walk out to the gate."

Loulie heard him. "Go on, you two. Alice can sleep on our bed until you get back."

"I want to hear the bell toll and watch the guards close up for the night," he said as we left the compound behind.

It was something we enjoyed doing even in the cold. People didn't seem to notice us quite so much during the moments when day turned into night and we savored not being required to face our foreignness for a little while.

On New Year's Day we spent some time reflecting over the past year and some more dreaming about the one to come. I wrote in my diary:

"We are now six families all told in our missionary community and we get along well. To have such companionable friends helps prevent homesickness and for this I thank the Lord, who knows how prone I am to that dreadful disease.

"The problem that arose between Loulie Scranton and me seems to have disappeared since the night Alice was born. We never spoke of whatever upset her but she acts just the same as before and I am so relieved."

The truth was she was jealous, which is why she reacted as she did when she saw our unpacked treasures. That green-eyed monster attacked us all at one time or another and often we didn't handle it well. We few lived so close and knew too much about each other's business.

That first cold winter Henry was frustrated beyond description because he couldn't preach from some high wooden pulpit and convince droves of Koreans to turn to God. No pulpit existed in Korea in 1886 and besides, the government forbade proselytizing and that's all there was to it. But back in the fall of 1885, a window of promise cracked open for Henry and let a little sunshine fall on his way. I remember when he returned from collecting our mail from the American Legation with news that had him bouncing on his toes.

"Ensign Foulke has done me a great good turn," he told me at top voice.

I was busy inspecting the letters he dropped into my lap and didn't respond. Foulke had been assigned to the American Legation, replacing Horace Allen, and so his actions always stimulated interest among us.

"Don't you want to know what it is?"

"What? Oh, sorry." I reluctantly laid aside the letters and gave Henry my full attention. "Tell me."

"Foulk, in an audience with the king, mentioned my presence in Seoul and told His Majesty I am here to offer Western-style education to young boys if he so wishes. He told His Majesty that I am willing to teach on my own account and do not expect the government to procure students for me. He said I'm anxious to know what the government and the people might think of such an arrangement."

The truth was, Henry had already begun teaching English to a small group of boys, and was doing so quietly and simply, but without first gaining official permission. So the news from Foulke encouraged Henry to believe that all would be well anyway.

"The king expressed pleasure that I'm here to help Korean people and he does not object to my teaching if I can get pupils and start a school on my own. That means royal sanction, Ella, to open a school! This will be known all over Korea soon and we'll have nothing to fear because the king knows about me and approves of my teaching. God is with us! And someday...I just know it...Koreans will hear gospel preaching and will turn to faith." He crackled with anticipation, his eyes afire with hope."

"I'm sure you're right, Henry. Freedom will come. People will learn about God. It's only a matter of time."

Even as I spoke, though, I wondered if he would not see his dreams and plans crushed many times beneath edicts, restrictions and someone else's ambitions.

Chapter 8

Potholes in the Road

"What are you doing, Ella?"

"Making a list."

"A list? Of what?"

"Things to order from America. I need thread, needles, pins, buttons...and we both need everyday handkerchiefs. Also, I need a new dress. Mine are falling into tatters." I spoke the last part softly hoping Henry wouldn't notice, but he did.

"New dress? Uh, I see...what kind?"

"Henry, I remember seeing the most beautiful blue watered silk at the dry goods store in Lancaster before we left. I wonder if Byron's wife, Mary, could find me some material like that."

"Silk, Ella?" Henry tilted his head, his eyes unfocused. Calculating costs. "Is that sensible?" Sensible? Sure it is. Well, silk may not be the most durable of fabrics but aren't I supposed to look nice?

"What do you mean, Henry? What do you consider sensible?"

"Ella, remember where we are and who we are. Seoul doesn't hold too many fashion parades, and...."

"What are you saying, Henry?" Irritation rising.

"Wouldn't some dark wool material be more appropriate?"

I gave in, of course—I did lots of that in those early days because Henry seemed six jumps ahead of me in knowing what we were about—and asked Mary to buy some *sensible* brown wool so that I might go *sensibly* about my missionary duties clad as any *sensible* woman would be in my circumstances.

Feeling more than a little spiteful about surrendering, without telling my husband I also asked Mary to send to me some calico and percale for everyday wear, but taking a *sensible* fit of my own, I asked for dark brown and blue prints because Seoul was so dirty that anything lighter would have amounted to sheer foolishness. Even I knew that.

Seoul was unspeakably filthy. I didn't like to talk about it because I was learning—and acting on it *sometimes*—that to dwell on unpleasantness only created more. But whether we talked about it or not, trash and garbage rotting in the streets, noxious liquids running along ditches and puddling in low spots all conspired to foul our clothes and dirty our shoes. That unspeakable mess threatened our lives as well. Smallpox raged all over the city. Drs. Scranton, Heron and Allen treated dozens of victims each day. I walked out of the compound only with a piece of cloth held over my nose and mouth to filter the air. I never took Alice anywhere except to Loulie's for tea.

Bright spots decorated the dreary from time to time, however. Late in January Horace Underwood received a Christmas package from his family. He invited Henry and me to his home along with the other expatriates to share the plum pudding they sent. I was keen to go because I'd recovered from Alice's birth and was fidgety from inactivity.

"Oh, what fun!" I said to Henry. "Let's go! Granny can watch Alice for an hour." We'd hired an older woman to help with the housework since the baby came.

Henry looked up from his language books and shook his head. "I can't," he said. "I promised myself I would learn this vocabulary list before tomorrow and...."

"But, Henry," I pleaded. "It's a party...he's your friend...."

"Please, Ella, you go anyway. It's just a step through the wall and you can walk over with Will and Loulie. I can't possibly make it. He'll understand. Horace needs ladies' company more than mine anyway.

He sees me all the time." Henry bent his head over the pages before him and I knew that if I said any more, he wouldn't hear me anyway.

Looking at him studying there in the lamplight I noticed something I hadn't caught before. Henry was thinner than when we left the U.S. His shirt collar stood away from his neck where it had always been so snug. Odd, I thought, for a man who loves to eat as much as he does. I picked up my shawl, kissed the top of his bent head and dashed over to Loulie's to walk with them to Horace's party.

I understood Henry's desire to learn Korean. I wanted to, too, but not as hotly as he did. He dreamed of preaching to Koreans in their own language, a dream probably given by the Lord although it was kept alive, I was sure, by his love of public speaking.

Competition may have entered in to the mix as well because Horace Underwood had a strong linguistic bent and everyone said he had the best language skills among our foreign community. Something in Henry reared up at that for he didn't want to be bested by his friend. Thinking about the two of them drew my mind deeper into myself as I compared Henry's strong religious fervor with my lack thereof. What made the difference between us? We both grew up in Christian homes and were taught to live by the Golden Rule. We both believed in God and behaved as good people do, most of the time at least. In spite of all that automatic righteousness, Henry burned to do, to be, more while I didn't even warm to the idea. Truth to tell, it seldom occurred to me and I wondered why.

Will and Henry persuaded our mission via long letters and bulky reports to buy more property nearby and Henry again found himself supervising workmen making repairs, this time for a boys' school. The king's approval of his teaching set him racing to prepare the premises and begin a real school, but the mechanics of doing business, especially banking, almost pushed him over the edge.

The problem? Our mission required that all bank accounts be kept in Japan for they felt that the unstable political situation threatened the safety of our funds. So when we needed cash we purchased

Mexican dollars in the port of Chemulpo, a day's journey from Seoul. Henry usually accompanied the dollars from the port and to the Seoul bank where he exchanged them for Korean cash, little brass coins worth next to nothing. When time came to pay workmen, the dear man came walking through the compound gate followed by a string of pony carts loaded with money that he dispensed to whoever was waiting. We figured it was their problem to haul it away.

After yet another performance of this burdensome, bothersome ritual I sensed Henry's boundless energy was flagging. "How does this part of your missionary work make you feel?" I asked him.

He heaved a deep sigh and rubbed a hand over his face. "Just the mere business of living consumes so much of our time..." He reached out from the rocking chair and put both arms around my waist. "... and this bothers me. Rather than preaching or teaching, instead of language study even, I must haul a ton of money across town or supervise ditch diggers or spend hours ordering collar buttons and canned meat. Does this please God? I sincerely hope so because it certainly does not please me."

———※———

Problems, perceived and real, blighted our days that spring. The perspective of time suggests some were trivial but that's a view I didn't know anything about then. Henry's work was Western education for the Koreans. We were thrilled by the king's acceptance of the idea and pleased with the collection of boys who came to learn. All well and good. But the fact that some other missionaries, our friends and fellow Christians, also opened schools side by side with Henry's brought my blood to the boiling point.

It wasn't fair. Even his dear friend, Horace Underwood, set up what he called an orphanage but whatever he called it, it was an educational institution and it was right beside Mrs. Scranton's girls' school. Mrs. Scranton and Henry worked together for the betterment of Korean boys and girls and why did Horace want to set up shop next door instead of in another part of town? What kind of friend would do that?

Then, adding insult to injury, three American teachers arrived at the request of the Korean government. Maybe they *were* invited even before we arrived but why did they have to show up to teach in the government school just as Henry's work was getting off the ground? What if they took all the students, leaving Henry looking like a fool?

These grievances made it difficult for me to remain civil when we all met at prayer meeting and Sunday worship. Rather than smile like a good sweet Christian as I'd been taught, I wanted in the worst way to say, "Why don't you remove yourselves off to the other side of Seoul? Begin a school at East Gate, or better yet, in Chemulpo." Wicked, unchristian feelings threatened to reduce missionary work to a competition, but I was so anxious that Henry's hours of hard work and his dreams for Korea succeed, that he be acknowledged as the unique and wonderful person I knew him to be.

Then there was the business of the lady doctor. The royal family appreciated Dr. Allen's treatment of the men but preferred a woman to care for the cloistered queen and court ladies. Dr. Allen's influence at the palace was enormous and we all knew that the group that acquired a lady doctor would enjoy an edge with the royals. I hoped our mission would be the one to acquire the needed doctor but, given my poor attitude about the schools and other rubs, I wondered how we all, especially me, would behave if we were bested by another group pulling off that particular coup.

All of this heaped up together made me aware that becoming a missionary does not guarantee sainthood. I honestly expected that it would and was disappointed to discover the same old me dwelt within my sensible clothes. A pity.

Late in April I stole one of Henry's workmen to dig flower beds in front of our house and then to lay sod (which he produced at my request and about the source of which I asked no questions) around the beds for a proper lawn. I planted seeds sent to us from home that kept arriving in letters all winter long.

While the workman and I were patting down the last of the sod Henry returned from the legation with the mail. I followed him into the house and was struggling with my stubborn hair when I heard a roar from the rocking chair, something like a grizzly bear with a sore toe.

"What in the world is the matter?"

"This," he shouted, "is the matter!" waving what was obviously a most offensive piece of paper. I waited, knowing he would continue.

"Those idiots in New York are asking me questions I answered for them months ago. Several letters disappeared...some of mine and at least one of theirs. What a disaster! "Money!" he continued. "Did they deposit it for us or didn't they? Do we have permission to prepare the school or don't we?"

What could I say in the face of his anguish? He'd been working at the school site from 5:30 in the morning until 7 at night, foregoing his precious language study to see it all done correctly. Now came these muddled communications casting doubt on the acceptability of what he was doing. There was no end in sight to the problems of doing business halfway round the world by flimsy bits of paper.

I stood by my husband's chair and pulled his head against me, wishing I could make all troubles disappear. As I rubbed his back I realized again that he was thinner than the man I married. I touched bones across his shoulders that I'd never felt before but he seemed healthy so I decided not to worry.

The next morning Henry was up and out at 5:30 as usual. After feeding and bathing Alice, she and I climbed the hill to see what was going on at the work site. When Henry saw us he shouted that we come and see.

"Do you realize what this means?" he asked as he waved his arm at the ground being leveled and graded by the workmen and their shovels. "Right in this place, young men, future believers, will not only learn English and Western thought, they will learn about the one true God and His redeeming Son, Jesus."

"How are you this morning, dear?" I had to know if the despair of lost letters still troubled him.

"What?"

"I asked how you are. If you recall, last evening you were a bit upset over the mail."

"Oh, that." He grinned and dismissed it all with a wave of his hand. "I decided not to worry about that any more. We are building for the Kingdom out here and it will be all right. I'm sure New York will stand by us, no matter what. They'll sort it out eventually."

And there he stood in the sunshine with his tilted world in balance once more, sure that every Korean within reach would meet the Creator.

───────■───────

When Easter Sunday arrived that spring the sun was warm, the sky a delicate blue and the weeping willows waved green boughs that looked like chiffon flung across a lady's shoulders.

One year earlier Henry and I had stepped ashore in Chemulpo, only to leave Korea short days later in ignominy and pain. Now, one year later we were meeting in Seoul for worship with our fellow expatriate Christians, housed, fed and hard at work. No new Easter bonnets appeared among us ladies—no bonnets at all, actually. Some of us packed them in our freight, incapable of imagining Sunday worship without a hat, but between the crush of packing and a few splashes of sea water, not a bonnet survived. So, bareheaded, we celebrated Christ's resurrection.

Adding to the joy of Easter was the baptism by Henry and Horace of our Alice and Marian Scranton, now a healthy little girl, her illness behind them. Following the babies was Mr. Tetzeya of the Japanese Legation who had studied the Bible with Henry for some time. He'd discovered and accepted Christianity as a student in northern Japan and pursued it during his diplomatic posting in Seoul. Now he wanted his decision to be made public.

Henry and I walked out to South Gate at sundown that day. This time he carried Alice in his arms, not caring that people would find the sight of us most curious, staring and commenting, unconcerned whether we heard them or not. Ignoring the milling crowds we reminisced about the year just past; then the great bell tolled, silencing our talk and stirring our memories while it sent Koreans scampering for home. Hushed, we too walked home while Alice slept in her father's strong arms.

Chapter 9

Baby Alice

Spring flourished in 1886, and so did our difficulties. In retrospect, most of them seem too trivial to mention, but back then? In our youth and inexperience, we felt pushed to the limit of our abilities to cope.

A contingent of French Catholics arrived in Korea, demanding religious tolerance from the government. Henry, implacable in his dislike for Romanists, ranted against their intrusion, pronouncing them "dictatorial and pompous."

Closer to home, a huge, fat louse hid under Alice's little arm. I discovered him during her bath. What would my mother have said? Either about that one or his twin curled beneath the waistband of my bloomers? Henry returned from a money-gathering trip to Chemulpo covered with itchy red welts from knees to toes. Flea bites. Probably acquired at the inn where he slept.

I spent my days, for the most part, isolated from Koreans. The mission board in New York assigned me, along with Loulie and other wives who joined us later, the role of "assistant missionary," but they forgot to define just how we should offer our assistance, a failure I'd have to deal with before long.

Late one May afternoon, however, when the sunlight was golden and the shadows long, my isolation was breached. The butcher's wife came to see our baby. She'd sent word ahead that she'd like to visit and of course I welcomed her. After all, haggling with her over bits of beef and pork in their fly-blown shop created a certain warmth and understanding between us. So she came...accompanied by six friends.

Cook made tea and served cookies. I pulled the dining chairs into a circle when I saw how many ladies were crowding through the door but they disdained the chairs and wandered about the room examining and touching all our things, which didn't please me too much although I fought to keep a smile on my face.

The biggest hit of our tea party, aside from Alice, was a mirror hanging in the sitting room. The butcher's wife (I didn't know her name. In Korean custom the exchange of names comes later on, if at all.) led the group in their inspection of our home and when in her travels around the room she discovered her reflection staring back at her from the mirror, she started in surprise and shrieked, "Ai-go! Ai-go!" which for Koreans voices a whole catalog of emotions. (I still say it when all else fails.)

The other women whisked to her side to see what she had found. They took turns twisting, waving, shaking their heads and discussing the clarity of this glass in a frame that showed their faces far better than the polished brass surfaces they were accustomed to.

About that time Henry came in from his school. He bowed politely to our guests, one eyebrow raised quizzically in surprise at the number and noise level in the room.

"Oh, darling, I'm so glad you're here," I muttered.

"How's everything going?" He could talk quietly when absolutely necessary.

"All right, I guess. I've never done this before, you know. Please talk to them. You understand Korean so much better than I."

As Henry chatted with the ladies for a moment, I went into the bedroom and brought Alice out to show her off. The women flocked around, eager to see and touch the foreign baby, the first one they'd ever seen.

"Ai-go, look at that."

"Isn't she fat?"

"Oh...oh, look. She's smiling."

Alice behaved like a perfect lady, enduring their probing hands and excited chatter. They fondled her hair, tugged on her hands and squeezed her legs. I knew their curious fingers itched to lift up her clothes and inspect her all over, and they may have done so had not Henry sat down at the little black pump organ and begun to play.

He pumped away with gusto and when the women abandoned Alice and clustered around him to see how he produced such intriguing sounds, he began to sing Charles Wesley's lively hymn, "O For a Thousand Tongues to Sing." The ai-gos flew thick and fast as the foreign master of that remarkable home sang for his wife's guests.

Henry's entertainment didn't stop with the butcher's wife and her friends; the workmen from the school heard the ruckus, dropped their tools and dashed across the yard to peer in through our open windows. Then, no sooner had Henry reached, "My gracious Master and my God, assist me to proclaim..." than the door popped open and in walked a Chinese man we had never seen before.

"Hello," he said in passable English. "I have just arrived by ship from Shanghai and heard your music as I was passing by."

He then strode across the sitting room, disdaining the straight dining chairs circled about for our guests' use, and pulled the rocker from the bedroom, the one we shipped out from home. He seated himself in the center of things and settled back in comfort to listen to Henry's singing.

But Granny, Alice's *amah* (nanny), would have none of that. She went for him, pried him out of the chair and dragged it back into the bedroom where it belonged. She shut the door with a snap, took Alice from my arms and stomped off to the kitchen with nary a glance at our cheeky guest. Considering that for centuries the Koreans had endured Chinese control, Henry and I agreed that our Granny was a plucky lady indeed.

After slurping our tea and obliterating the cookies, our guests— ladies and Chinese stranger—took their leave en masse. When the last visitor had cleared the compound gate Henry and I sat on the edge of the porch to talk over our little party.

"You know, Henry, I really like these people. Even though they do things we think are rude, there's a...a directness about them that I find appealing."

"You're right, of course," he replied. "I get so exasperated at times...but, truth be told, I probably drive them crazy as well. It's just that we grew up so differently, learned such radically different things from our parents, and then those ideas and principles clash mightily when we come together."

We both agreed we'd enjoyed true and honest fun that afternoon, suspecting the butcher's wife and her friends might have picked up some new information about us as well.

Letters shaped the core of our existence in Korea: receiving or sending, doing business or ministry, expressing love and exchanging news. They nourished us, keeping us alive like food and oxygen. Henry showed me one he wrote to his Drew Seminary classmate, Julian Wadsworth. "You must not let it out," he wrote, "but I am not nearly the man I was physically when I bade you goodbye. I cannot do the work I did at home. There is something wrong somewhere. I may be better when I am acclimated. Do not think from this that I am sick or my health is undermined. I don't believe it is."

He went on to explain how important it was, in his thinking, that we reproduce as nearly as possible the living conditions we were accustomed to at home and which we tried to do with varying degrees of success. We learned this in Japan during our months with the missionaries and as yet had discovered nothing to make us think otherwise.

I pondered Henry's comment to Julian about becoming acclimated to Korea. How long does it take to acquire acclimation? We'd been in Korea over a year and away from home since a year ago Christmas. Was Henry's thinness and lack of energy due to being in a strange new place, or was he ill?

Horace Underwood banged on the door mid-May, and then stepped into our sitting room, his stubborn hair defying its pomade.

"Today's Buddha's birthday. Let's walk out and watch the lantern parade."

Henry stared at his friend and I could see him see-sawing between participating in a heathen celebration and wanting to see whatever it was the Koreans were doing that night. Curiosity won over rectitude.

"Yes, let's do it," he said, abandoning his dictionary.

I told Granny to watch Alice and we picked up Will Scranton and John Heron on our way out of the compound. Their pregnancies prevented Loulie and Harriet from coming, too.

The Buddhist Lantern Festival pleased us all with the sight of brilliant flames of light within hundreds of colored paper lanterns hanging from gates and from bamboo poles carried by the faithful through the streets. The evening ended with fireworks, which we watched from atop South Gate. The red-and-blue clad guards invited us to climb the steps at the side of the magnificent old thing, so we stood on the second story veranda to watch Roman candles light up the black velvet sky.

We caught sight of Dr. and Mrs. Allen strolling below with Lt. Foulk from the American Legation. "Oh, look," I exclaimed. "Shall we go down and greet them?"

"If you do," Horace growled, "you go without me."

The anger and hostility in his voice and the set of his jaw took me aback. Henry grasped my elbow and put his lips close to my ear. "Let it go, Ella," he muttered. I remembered Loulie's words, "Big trouble."

Talk abounded about problems within the medical group. Like the Scrantons, John Heron and his wife, Harriet, had evidently had nothing but grief in their association with the Allens. Horace Underwood hadn't escaped either. His surly refusal to greet them proved that. At that time I didn't delve into their difficulties. After all, they all belonged to the same mission, and I felt we, in ours, had enough on our own plates to keep us occupied.

Difficulties notwithstanding, Henry's school opened officially and he proudly proclaimed that his "missionary work" had begun. The poor dear struggled against the necessity of spending so much time in the business of living—house and school repair, food ordering, language learning—all crucial to our survival but to him they did not constitute missionary work and therefore forged a burden he bore without tolerance or joy.

But with the school open and students coming to study English and other subjects in a proper building rather than around our table, I too was grateful for that beginning, not only for my dear husband's sake, but also because I sensed that building friendly relationships was the way to Korean hearts. First they needed to like us and trust us, and then they would listen to our good news.

Other people were working hard, too. Mrs. Scranton, whatever I may have felt about her personally, was tireless. I sometimes wondered what the Korean people thought about her solemn face. Deep frown lines between her eyebrows gave me an involuntary sense that I must have broken some rule. Did Koreans feel that way, too?

Perhaps not, because she began her women's work with a rather diverse pair of students: one a nobleman's wife, the other an orphan girl of the Topsy sort who just grew without family nurture. Both of them seemed happy to be learning from the tall, buxom American lady despite her perpetual frown.

"Ah, I do admire that woman's stamina. What strength of character!" Henry exulted one day when our paths intersected hers on the compound.

"You would," I muttered spitefully. He didn't hear me. Henry often exclaimed about Mrs. Scranton and didn't seem to mind that I didn't join in with his enthusiasms.

Will Scranton had already opened his own clinic and was seeing more and more patients. It saddened me that Heron and Scranton couldn't work with Dr. Allen. But I had learned through snippets of conversation that he put off anyone who dared to invade his sphere of work and influence, a proud and prickly individual. Nevertheless, our little group of youngsters—none of us had seen age 30 yet—was off and running, doing this and that in an effort to show Koreans that God loves them.

Rainy season broke upon us in July. Henry closed the school and everything slowed to a snail's pace. I tried hard to get him to rest—no success.

One Sunday while rain poured down outside, Horace Underwood dipped up a handful of water and in Herons' sitting room baptized the first Korean convert to Protestant Christianity. Henry assisted. On our way to the service I couldn't resist asking him a question. "How does it make you feel that the first convert is Horace's?"

He paused a long moment, our promise to talk openly with each other warring with his natural reticence. "It's all right," he said finally. "I just thank God that this man accepted Jesus as savior...no matter who was the instrument of grace." I should've known.

Mr. Noh, the convert, curious about Christianity, had stolen a copy of the gospels from Horace Allen's office, and had then gone to Horace Underwood for more information. The visits turned into a catechism class and Noh began to attend our worship and prayer times, stretching his sketchy English comprehension to its limit. Then he asked for baptism, thereby publicly acknowledging his acceptance of and commitment to Christianity.

Noh risked much by this, exposing himself to the wrath of his fellow Koreans. At the close of the baptism service we all stood and pledged ourselves to pray for our new brother in the Lord.

Sarah Ann, the Herons' new baby, was also baptized by Horace and Henry, and then Henry preached to us all. He had a wonderful time. The big question in my mind and in his, I know, was, How long before he is allowed to preach to Koreans?

Rain bucketed down, mud and corruption deepened in the streets and cholera again ravaged the city. Hundreds of people died all around us. We could hear the mourners wailing on the city wall nearby. Henry's language teacher said the dead must be carried out of Seoul through either West Gate or Little East Gate. None of the other gates could be used for such grim purposes.

Differences forgotten in the emergency, all three doctors had more to do than they could manage. I seldom left the house and finally even Henry kept close to home, reading and studying. Sleep was hard to come by. I got up time after time through the night to lay my hand on Alice's little head to check for fever...and dear Henry's as well.

None of us caught it, thank God.

Chapter 10

Teamwork Under Construction

During those steamy, pestilence-ridden days, we stayed home as much as possible which gave us time to talk. We grappled together over a question about his students at the school.

"Help me think this through, Ella." He knew by now that I have a head for figures. "How much financial aid should I give to the boys who want to study with me?"

"How much do you have in the budget for this kind of aid?"

"Budget? Um...well, uh...I'm not sure..."

We both knew that most Koreans were poor and education, though valued, was difficult to come by. In the government school close by all the boys were clothed and fed with government funds. This of course affected Henry's thinking and that of others starting up mission schools.

"But that's not the only issue," Henry told me as we compared ourselves to the government school. "Neither is budget." He dismissed my bookkeeperly ways with a wave of his hand, out of character with his usual miserliness when it came to household expenses or blue silk dresses.

"How much *ought* we to give?" he pondered. "To support a student out and out without making him feel responsibility in the matter is clearly a mistake."

"Yes, but..." I began.

"Yes, but to refuse to help someone who is making every effort to help himself but cannot manage is to err in the other direction."

"I couldn't have said it better myself," I muttered, unheard.

We arrived at no quick solution after gnawing on the issue from all sides. Henry wound up the conversation by pronouncing that the Lord would give illumination. He did do this eventually but at the time how I wished He would provide us with some instant guidelines. We were struggling to build our mission work in Korea, with no precedents to follow and no predecessors to counsel us. So we floundered along in our ignorance, knowing only that we must do something and feeling in a rush to do it *now*.

Meanwhile the plague crept closer, turning into more than a dark, distant threat looming outside our walls. The gateman banged on our door one morning and asked to talk with Henry. He wouldn't come in so the two of them stood in the drenching rain under umbrellas made of oiled paper and bamboo.

"A little girl is sick by Grandmother Scranton's house."

"Is her family caring for her?" Henry asked him.

"No family. She has no one."

"Tell the doctor. He will know what to do."

"She needs medicine. No family." The gateman plodded off toward the clinic to tell Will that a cholera-stricken child waited for him within the walls that until now he had hoped would protect his family and all of us from the pestilence that ravaged the city.

Later that day the little girl in her delirium and fever took off all her clothes and crawled out under the large tree beside the house Mrs. Scranton used for home and school. She lay there in the rain.

Henry saw her. "She can't stay there. I've got to do something." He rounded up two coolies to help him put the girl into a room at the clinic. I dashed across to Loulie's, needing not to be alone with my fears.

"The poor little thing, not a soul cares what happens to her," Loulie's sympathies, like mine, yearned to right the wrongs of poverty and disease.

"It's so hard to know what to do," I added. "I can tell you honestly I'm terrified that Alice will catch it, or your little Marian. Then where would we be?"

"I know." She was silent for a moment, and then jumped to her feet. "Let's go out to the pill house and get some clothes. We put some out there to give away."

We pulled some stockings, bloomers and an old muslin dress from the stack of used clothing in Will Scranton's pill house. The poor sick child understood we were trying to help her and put up her hands like a baby when we slipped the dress over her head. Then she lay back on the floor pillows in her little clinic room and I spread a sheet over her.

"Mool," she croaked, without opening her eyes. "Water." Loulie brought some to her in a tumbler and I leaned her against my shoulder while she drank.

We spoke not a word between us as we left the clinic. On the path before we parted to go to our own homes we stared at each other for a long moment and I know our thoughts were identical.

What have I done? Will this one small act of decency infect my family and me? Will Alice, Marian, Henry or Will sicken and die because of me? Loulie and I each turned and dragged ourselves home. As soon as I opened my door, I shouted for help.

"Hot water! Boil some water! I must bathe and I want you to boil these clothes I'm wearing."

Both the cook and the amah looked at me askance. Hot bath in the middle of the day? In this weather? What is wrong with Honorable Wife? Shock turned to red-faced horror as I stripped off my clothes in the middle of the room and walked with them in my hand to the kitchen and tossed them into the big copper boiler we used on wash day. Terror made me angry and harsh.

"Boil these," I shouted. "And heat water. I must bathe *now*!" Cook scampered to bring me a robe from the bedroom and, eyes on the floor, she whispered, "Alice is sleeping."

"Thank God for that." I didn't know how I would've handled her demands to be picked up and fondled in my polluted state but that crisis I was not required to deal with.

Later, after I scrubbed myself and dressed again, I sank into the rocking chair in the serene sanctuary of our bedroom. I took a deep breath and began to shake like the last autumn leaf on a sugar maple tree. What ifs flooded my brain and questions engulfed me. What am I doing in this dreadful place? Why did we leave Pennsylvania? Is this truly what God wants of us? How can we be sure? Are these perils of disease and death part of His plan? Doesn't He know I'm too weak and fearful to deal with it all? Why me, God?

The Almighty did not seem to respond to my whys. My trembling did slow and then stop, however, and rocking in the chair soothed me at last. Alice slept on in her clean, white bed while rain drummed on the roof.

Four days later the little girl died. Henry blocked my going to tend her by saying he would take care of everything; no simple task, it turned out.

"I couldn't get the coolies to go near her," he told me later, "so I covered her naked body myself with the clothes you and Loulie found for her. Then I sent for the district magistrate but he, clever fellow, is in the country. His office returned my note unopened."

I burst into tears, brokenhearted by the lostness, the loneliness of the poor little girl. She couldn't even be buried properly. Henry ignored my tears, wrestling as he was with his own emotions. "I found two more coolies, paid them 3,000 cash *(the little Korean coins with the square hole in the center)* and $1.50 Mexican to bury her. I accompanied them myself to be sure the task was completed."

Henry scrubbed himself all over, as I had done, although he kept to the bedroom, out of sight of the helpers. We boiled his washable clothes. I brushed and sunned (the rain let up for a few hours) his trousers and jacket, praying the whole time that God would protect us from infection and wondering if He was listening. As we tried to arm ourselves against the pestilence that gripped Seoul, we both sank deep into sadness and depression. Seeing how a friendless one died in that land laid a heavy weight on our souls, one not easy to shake off.

We could not live forever under that cloud, though, and gradually learned to view our physical problems philosophically and with humor even, though I would've preferred it be at someone else's expense rather than my own.

Later that summer I woke with some internal distress. I was turning over in my mind the question of what to do when our bed began to shake. What was going on? I sat up and as I did Henry turned over to face me. I discovered by the moonlight shining through the bedroom window that he was laughing.

"What on earth is so funny?" I scolded.

"Oh, dear Ella," he chuckled as he sat up and put his arms around me. "You are making the most extraordinary sounds."

I struggled indignantly but he held me fast. "You beast! A gentleman would never speak of such things."

"Ah, dear lady, but I am no gentleman. I am a Pennsylvania farmer, a money changer, an English teacher and a repairer of stinking old houses. And your insides sound exactly like the cannon's roar from a United States man o' war. Forgive my laughter but it is just too funny."

I flounced out of bed for two reasons: one, I didn't want him to see me smiling just yet, and two, I had to go out back to the privy and that most quickly.

I spent a couple of days in bed with frequent and distressing bouts of diarrhea. Henry, after timing my attacks with his pocket watch, brought me medicine from Dr. Scranton. The problem diminished and although I felt weak I got up and around before long. No doubt the midnight laughter helped the healing process although I waited for some time before I admitted it.

Just as hints of autumn replaced that long, hard summer of 1886, the first box arrived that we ordered from America. Its coming was not without problems—was anything without problem in those days?—

for it had been dumped into the Yokohama harbor en route. And once the poor box reached Korea the shipping agent in Chemulpo, in direct contradiction to Henry's orders, took out all the contents, made bundles of them and sent them to us by pony.

Henry fussed at length over the countermanding of his direction but we succumbed at last to our eagerness to open the bundles and get at our new things. I can see it yet. Henry's collars looked as though they had been dragged through the mud all the way from Chemulpo to Seoul. On the other hand, Alice's new shoes and clothes plus some items of mine did not suffer from their saltwater bath in Yokohama harbor. Then Henry reached for a box I recognized.

"Don't touch that!" I screeched.

He jumped as though burned. "Why not? What's wrong?"

"I must open this one. Close your eyes."

The dear man stood in the middle of the floor, eyes squeezed shut and a most bewildered look on his face. I opened the box and drew out a sturdy jacket I'd asked Father to buy for him. It was in perfect condition, untroubled by the dunking in Japan.

"Put your arms behind you and don't open your eyes, no matter what you feel happening," I said. Then I pulled the sleeves onto his arms and the jacket up across his shoulders and walked around to see how it looked.

"Perfect. You may open your eyes now."

Henry looked first at the tweed sleeves of his new jacket, and then brushed both hands down its lapels. He looked at me then at the warm wool coat he wore.

"Look in the mirror."

He walked over to the wall mirror, the one that had entranced our Korean visitors, and inspected his new jacket in the glass.

"It's wonderful, Ella. This winter when I study or work late it will keep me blessedly warm. Ah, what a lucky man I am!"

He gathered me up in a bear hug and whirled me off my feet. Alice, watching from her spot on the floor, laughed and crowed and clapped her hands.

We dug through the bundles, discovering things we did not order, items chosen by loving friends and family at home. What joy! Some wallpaper, though, a gift from my family, suffered badly from the seawater. I was crushed by its condition and Henry, trying to cheer me up, said, "But there is lots and lots of it. Now, if we make sure the paperhanger has plenty of tobacco *(would a missionary sanction smoking by those he employs?)*, and if he looks wise long enough and if you give him plenty of time to work—don't rush him—he will make a good job of it."

Henry was not so cheerful over the ruination of a beautiful white silk handkerchief, a rare gift from his mother. He vowed to make the shipping company pay for its loss.

What a time we had, opening and inspecting our treasures and trying to discover what could be salvaged and mourning over what could not. Simple items we took for granted back home assumed great charm and value for us at that distance. Our perspective had shifted radically along with our move to the other side of the world where availability of the commonest things was only a memory.

The summer of 1886, however, wasn't through with us yet. On top of cholera, death, summer heat mixed with endless monsoon rains, and waterlogged bundles from home, a new political crisis set our world a-buzz.

The Korean king banished four young officials from their posts at court. Why? Because they associated too regularly with foreigners like us. His action suggested that our presence displeased His Majesty and he told us so by this oblique, Asian method that, although it didn't touch us overtly, conveyed his negative feelings about us nonetheless. And we wondered, did the banishment and implied criticism of us come from the king himself or by pressure from Chinese advisers at court, Mandarins who represent the conservative, anti-modernization side of the ongoing difficulties in Korea?

Many of the nations represented in Seoul by legations and consulates resented the implications of the banishment and some teetered on the brink of pronouncing their governments insulted by the action, so Horace Allen, who seemed to have privileged insight of such matters told us.

"Only God knows," he muttered, "where formal insults between governments can lead in this tinderbox land."

Dr. Allen also told us to prepare for the worst. As we discussed just what that might entail, Will Scranton declared, "Well, going on that advice, I shall clean up my rifle and pack a valise."

Although we had no rifle to clean up Henry hauled out from storage a couple of small valises, dusted them off and set them on the floor in our bedroom. We filled one mainly with diapers for Alice. Then as we dashed about from house to house talking and preparing, we learned that twenty U.S. Marines came up to Seoul from Chemulpo where our old friend, the USS Ossipee, was in port. Captain McGlensy had to take action to protect us missionaries after all, whether he wanted to or not. I should've liked to encounter him again in these circumstances.

No sooner had the Marines deployed around our legation than word reached us that the king had recalled the banished officials and reinstated them in their former positions. That fanned our speculation once again. Did this mean the liberal, pro-modernization Japanese advice had won over Chinese suggestion?

Whoever had the upper hand at the moment, poor little Korea was pushed one way and then another by more powerful countries who cared not a whit for the welfare of the Land of the Morning Calm. Will this peninsula's people ever stand tall and strong, respected by the rest of the world? I wondered.

I tried to relax and let the cooler air of September deal with my anxieties as I unpacked our little bags and put Alice's diapers back in the drawer. A promise Jesus spoke to His friends just before they strode off into an unknown future whispered in my thoughts for days. "Lo, I am with you always," He'd said to them.

Could this, did this, apply to me as well?

Chapter 11

A "Dangerous Foreigner"

Little Alice emerged from infancy that autumn and showed us what a strong individual she was. I noticed the changes as she began pulling herself up by the furniture and then lurched into her first independent steps, arms waving and jaw clenched with huge determination. Granny scuttled around behind her, clucking and fussing with arms outstretched ready to catch and coddle in case the baby fell.

"Don't worry," I urged her. "She'll be all right. All babies do this. Just leave her alone."

"Yes, yes." Granny would nod and agree...and go on doing as she pleased. She set herself to prevent any mishap that might cause Alice to whimper. She'd obviously decided long since that she knew far more about child care than I did, which may have been true, but I was not prepared to admit it. The issue, in my thinking then, was simple insubordination. While she humored me to my face and nodded acquiescence to my orders, she ignored what I told her and always, always did what she thought best.

This irritated me, frazzling my soul until I suspect, if one could see souls, mine would have looked like my runaway hair. There was no order or serenity at all. Whose baby was this, anyway? And my irritation was as hard for me to deal with as Granny's insubordination. I determined to exhibit a Christian spirit before that non-Christian woman if it killed me, and everyone knew such an exhibition did not include losing one's temper, which I came close to doing daily.

But didn't Jesus undergo human emotions? How I wanted to believe He did, although I never heard any preacher or Sunday school teacher say so. How did He act when someone in his family rubbed him the wrong way? How did He feel when His disciples missed a point He was making, or when they failed to trust Him? Was He always and forever patient and kind?

Perhaps He was, but I suspected—and yes, I hoped—He felt the rising tides of exasperation and irritation like I did. After all, the Bible said our Lord was tempted just as we are and I decided that if I could feel sure He grappled with temper as I did, then I wouldn't feel so isolated and so unworthy.

I couldn't know for sure how Jesus would react to Granny's polite mutiny, so I decided it all boiled down to what *I* did when tempted to stamp my foot and shriek out my displeasure at the sweet old thing. I determined to contain myself and remain as serene as possible. Meanwhile, my child threatened to become a spoiled little so-and-so.

While I stewed around about how to deal with Granny and our daughter, Henry was happily preparing a sermon. He'd been invited to preach at the U.S. Legation at the invitation of Dr. and Mrs. Allen. Their baby son, Maurice, was to be baptized and all Americans were invited to worship there for the occasion.

In my opinion, one difficulty marred the scene. Horace Underwood's mission group remained sundered by conflict and disagreement and I couldn't imagine them sitting down in God's presence together. Would our friendship with Horace make it seem that Henry had taken sides?

"What will you do?" I asked him after the messenger had delivered the invitation.

"Do? I shall preach, of course." When I opened my mouth to ask him about Horace and his problems with Dr. Allen, Henry waved a hand at me and continued.

"I mentioned it to Horace straightaway and he urged me to do it, saying—correctly so, I might add—that their fracas is none of my affair."

At any rate, attendance was large and Henry preached on Elijah, the Tishbite. He went on for more than half an hour but so far as I could tell, everyone stayed awake.

One insignificant incident that morning left me struggling for composure. As we left the legation, Dr. Allen stood at the door saying goodbye. I put out my hand to shake his, as we do in Pennsylvania, but when he took it in his he bowed over it and kissed it as I understand they do in Europe.

"Thank you for coming, Ella. You look lovely," he said.

"Why, Dr. Allen...nothing of the sort...." And then, dreadful moment, I giggled like a simpering school girl. Could I please die? What a ridiculous moment!

Henry grasped my elbow and guided me down the steps and toward the gate. "Yes, Ella, you do look lovely," he said. "I see I'm going to have to watch our American representative a bit more closely...or learn the fine art of hand kissing."

"Well, tra-la, my good sir." We were through the gate and on safer ground. "He who knows how to treat a lady gets far in this life, as you can plainly see."

I felt as if someone had sprinkled some cinnamon and nutmeg on the plain custard of my life and, silly me, I enjoyed the flavor immensely.

The special meeting at the legation was unusual in a sense, but common in another, for we English-speaking foreigners had met together to worship each Sunday since we arrived in Korea. Within the first year we organized into a union church complete with constitution and pastors. Henry worked on the organizing committee and was elected first pastor.

"Are you pleased?" I asked him.

"More than I can tell you. It's an honor to pastor a union church where there is as much harmony as there is with us now. Surely the Lord will grant us a prosperous and successful year."

I kept still when he spoke of harmony although I was thinking about Horace's troubles within his group. Maybe Henry needs to believe that all is love and light amongst the missionaries, I decided. He knew better, though, because he and Horace had discussed the problems regularly and at length, and I had heard some of their discussions.

The leaves were gone and the mud frozen when Henry burst into the house shouting about a new crisis.

"Ella? Ella, listen to this!"

"In here," I called from the bedroom. "Keep your voice down, would you? Alice just began her nap." By then we'd repaired another room in our rambling old house and turned it into a nursery so Alice no longer slept in our room.

Henry flopped into the rocking chair and began rubbing the back of his neck. "I've just learned that I am regarded as one of three dangerous foreigners in Korea. Someone told this to the king, who mentioned it to Dr. Allen, and of course Allen was only too happy to pass the word along to someone who would tell me."

"Dangerous? Oh, dear." Fear packed the pit of my stomach with ice. "Why are you dangerous? What does this mean?"

For once Henry was not impatient with my questions. For once he was quiet, contemplative, unsure of what to do or say. "The reasoning, so I'm told, is that I am neither foreign official nor doctor and am therefore suspected of being a missionary."

Both of us sank into silence, he in the chair and I on the edge of our bed, as we mulled over what this kind of talk could mean to us. Korea still remembered the hundreds of people martyred some years earlier for embracing Catholicism. The teachings of Christianity (and at that time all Korean officials knew was the Roman version) appeared to threaten their authority. A law still on the books pronounced that anyone accepting or promoting Christianity must be put to death.

I suspected that the ongoing political tug-of-war between progressive Japanese and conservative Chinese came into play there.

For example, although Japan as a nation was clearly committed to its religions, the Japanese consul invited Henry to his home to teach a class on Christianity. His wife was Christian and he wanted to learn more. The Japanese were more open to the modernizing influence of the West even if it meant tolerating Western thought and religion.

On the other hand, conservative Chinese leaders struggled to maintain their grip on Korea, which meant screening out any outside influence that could undermine their purposes. In their thinking, the introduction of Christianity along with Western learning and medicine posed serious threats.

Our personal stake in these machinations? Most important, what could result from them pronouncing Henry a dangerous element? Would someone stir up a mob against us? How should we protect ourselves against the hideous possibilities?

I reached for Henry's hand and opened my mouth to pose these questions when he thumped the arms of the rocker with both fists and jumped to his feet.

"A dangerous foreign missionary, am I? I admit the charge. I shall keep right on with my work because I am convinced nothing serious will come of it. Don't wait dinner for me, Ella, I'll be late."

He scooped up his raincoat—the one in whose folds I caught raindrops on board ship and which had kept me dry from ship to shore in Chemulpo—shoved his arms into its sleeves as he kicked his feet into his shoes at the door and headed back up to the school.

I stared out after him. What will become of us? Will this threat pass us by as did cholera and the last set of rumors that had us packed and ready to leave? Will we ever feel secure, at home, safe in this perpetual tumult and strife? Was "lo, I am with you always" still in the Bible? And what did Jesus really mean by being with me? I had no idea.

Thanksgiving shone a warm lamp on us for a brief time. We Americans decided to take the day off—the doctors and teachers made their rounds, of course—and gather for a meal. Eighteen of us sat around an expanded Appenzeller table to eat. (We'd worshipped in the morning; Horace Underwood preached.) To create the table I propped up boards on either end and borrowed all the white tablecloths I could find. Between the Scrantons and us, including Mrs. Scranton, Senior, we scraped together enough chairs for everyone and in the lamplight it all looked quite festive.

No turkey, naturally, so I roasted a huge slab of beef, leaving it on all day. It turned out surprisingly tender. I discovered sweet potatoes in South Gate Market so tried my hand at candied yams. Limited success. Oh, they were sweet, all right, but very stringy. Cook made lovely yeast rolls by then and we had mounds of them so our dinner was ample, as was Henry's prayer before we ate. I sat too far away from him to nudge him to stop. Poor planning.

Alice had a wonderful time with all the other children. They all squealed and jumped about completely out of hand. We mothers just gave up and consigned them all to the servants who assembled from all the homes to help. To be in complete charge of the children pleased Granny and her cohorts no end. It pleased me, too, truth to tell, because my hands were full with dinner for so many guests.

After eating, we women walked away from the messy table and left it to the servants to clean up. From the sound of things they had a jolly time in the kitchen washing dishes, eating leftovers and discussing their employers.

"Let's sing a little, shall we?" Henry sat down at the pump organ and soon had us singing our hearts out. No hymnals necessary for we all knew the words to the old hymns he chose, each one familiar and dear to us. Korea and her problems, her threats against us, and our confusion as to what to do all retreated for a time. Conflicts and disagreements, jealousy and pain seemed far, far away and we were just a circle of friends enjoying a warm room and each other.

"Ella, the 'dangerous missionary' rumors are affecting the school," Henry told me as we stood at the window watching a few lazy snowflakes collect on South Gate's tiled roof.

"How, Henry?"

"The boys sent a delegation to me asking that the school be put on a government basis. When I asked them why, they said a report is going around that ours is a mission school.

"Three boys already left because they fear persecution, which means beheading if they are known to attend a mission school."

"Do you think they know about the law against Christianity?"

"Oh, yes, they certainly do."

I leaned my forehead against the cold glass while the same old questions marched across my mind, the whys that I could never answer.

"I shall do all I can to give this school a proper standing," Henry said as he began pacing back and forth, "but it seems to me that the very thing which ought to distinguish it gives the offence.

"I'm not worried." By now he was talking more to himself than to me. "Being under fire will in all probability be a good thing...and I shall trust the Lord to help me bravely bear it all."

What is so good about being under fire? It took me years to learn the answer to that one.

Our second wedding anniversary and Christmas came and went. Henry and I felt a little less bereft this time around, perhaps because we entertained more and spent less time feeling sorry for ourselves. We also received several letters from home, which helped.

On our anniversary Henry woke me early and asked me to walk out with him to South Gate. At first I couldn't think why he suggested exercise so early when he knows I don't wake up until much later. Then from the warmth of our bed I watched him fumble a small packet into his pocket. I understood and crawled out to accompany him.

When we reached the gate, Henry was disappointed. "I thought going so early we would have the gate all to ourselves," he grumbled. He wanted to climb up the steps and watch the winter sun light up the mountains to the north of Seoul.

But such was not to be. Oh, the sun-tipped peaks were beautiful against the blue sky but we were not alone in their presence, not by any means.

Hard by South Gate was a market that opened at dawn. Daily the *changsas* or merchants unload their carts and open their bundles of goods at the same time as we arrived for our tryst. The noise and roiling dust they created did not foster romance. Henry glared at them all for a moment. Fortunately none of the crowd noticed us, occupied as they were in setting up shop just inside the city wall.

"Come around to this side." Henry pulled me away from the market crowd and we walked through the gate and along the wall to a small grove of gnarled old pine trees that had long ago forgotten how to stand straight.

"Oh, Ella," he moaned. "I know how you love that gate and I wanted to begin this day with you in a place you enjoy. But..." He gestured helplessly at the noisy, teeming market crowd.

"I understand, dear," I responded. "You had a beautiful idea and certainly cannot be blamed that the merchants of Seoul are so uncooperative."

He reached into his pocket and held out to me the tiny package I saw him put there back at the house. "I sent to Japan for this. You do without so much that is beautiful and elegant, and I wanted something you could look at and wear and know how thankful I am that you consented to be my wife."

The impulse to giggle I'd been struggling with ever since I saw the market people intruding on our anniversary celebration died away as I unfolded the wrapping. Within it lay a pearl ring, one small, pale, lustrous pearl set in gold. I slipped it onto the third finger of my left hand where it nestled against my wedding band.

"Henry, it is so perfect, so beautiful!"

"Does it fit?" He looked so proud and yet just a touch unsure. Pulpits and schoolrooms were more comfortable to my husband than moments of sentiment and romance, yet he planned this wonderful moment for me to let me know how much he cared.

Rather than answer I held out my hand to him so he could see. He took it, raised it to his lips and kissed it, right where the two rings encircled my finger. "I love you, Ella," he whispered, his eyes like stars.

"And I love you." And because it seemed to me we had said all that was needed, that each of us knew what lay in the other's heart, I curtsied in response to Henry's kiss.

"Now shall we leave our South Gate to the *changsas* and go home to breakfast?" I asked.

He picked up my tone. "By all means, Mistress Appenzeller. My arm?"

Off we strolled toward home through the dirt and sewage of Seoul, my new pearl ring gleaming against the rough tweed of Henry's jacket.

Chapter 12

PaiJai School

Korean winters lasted forever, an eternity it seemed to me. Oh, the sun shone half-heartedly most days and I didn't mind the cold outside because our house was snug and warm. I guess I missed color most of all. The tiled and thatched roofs of Seoul were either gray or the nameless neutral of weathered-out straw. Every person I saw in the streets wore white. No one dressed in bright color except the occasional wealthy child one might chance to see or perhaps a wedding procession, which was more rare in my world than wealthy children. I was told that royal processions flaunted banners and robes of red, blue and yellow, but they never wound through our mission compound so I never saw one in those early years.

Mud, dirt, sewage and refuse filled the streets and trees shook bare black arms at the glowering sky. I sent Granny to the market to buy what we needed because I found no attraction in going there; besides, she could bargain far better than I could.

How gloomy I became. More than once I thanked God for Alice's chatter. Although not much of it made sense early on, she did love to talk. Her word mix between English and Korean confused us all and her bright baby laughter could dissolve my gloom as the south wind drives away rain clouds. She scattered sunshine wherever she went. I could forgive her ceaseless curiosity and her stubborn spirit when she spread light and joy through our lives like a silver knife spreads jam on toast.

An event arose that winter of 1887 that put a shine on my life for a few charming hours. A number of us were invited by the queen, no less, to a skating party at the palace. Annie Ellers, the not-quite medical doctor (she did *not* graduate from medical school no matter what her co-workers claimed) in Korea with Horace Underwood's mission served the medical needs of the women at court and brought the invitation to us foreigners to come and skate on their lake.

"Oh, darling, we must certainly go! What shall I wear?" Annie was barely out the door after delivering the queen's invitation when I began to dither. Henry and Horace had been working on their Bible translation at the table until the demands of society broke into their solemn task. Both looked up with frowns.

"Wear?" Ever quick to respond to any question, Horace said, "I suggest you wear plenty of warm clothes and never mind fashion. Otherwise you'll freeze."

A new, worse problem nearly broke my heart. "Oh, dear," I wailed. "We have no skates! We can't go after all...."

"There are Korean skates, silly. Send the gateman out to buy you some." Again Horace strode into the gap but his idea was so good that I forgave him for calling me silly.

Horace went reluctantly home to ready himself for the party and Henry sent the gateman to South Gate Market armed with drawings of our feet to buy us ice skates. He returned within the hour with a single pair.

"No skates this big," he explained as he handed Henry's drawing back to him.

"Don't feel badly, Ella," Henry said, for he had already read my mind. "I shall slide about on the ice in my boots and we'll have a fine time. We won't miss a visit to the palace just because of my big feet."

Twelve of us Americans walked through the palace gates along with seven or eight Germans. Henry carried my skates and clinging to his arm I felt like a girl again. Annie Ellers directed us to the lake—a pond really—which surrounded a beautiful open pavilion with crimson pillars.

As we strapped on our skates and shouted greetings to early arrivals already taking test glides across the ice, a flurry arose from the far side of the pavilion where several individuals I assumed were court attendants had gathered. Then, to my wonder and amazement, their Majesties walked into the pavilion and seated themselves on low chairs, apparently having come to watch the foreigners at play.

Dr. Allen and Annie Ellers both stood quietly until the royal countenances turned in their direction (the rest of us caught on finally and followed their example) then they (and we) bowed deeply and slowly. When I peeked at Henry out of the corner of my eye as we all paused at the bottom of our bow I could sense he was deeply moved and impressed to be allowed into the presence of the king and queen of Korea.

Again following the example of Annie and Dr. Allen, after paying our respects in the acceptably subservient manner, those of us who wore skates began sedately to move to and fro on the ice. Henry felt a bit shy after all about skittering around without skates and so was inspecting the stonework surrounding the pond until he discovered that a couple of the German guests also had feet too large for Korean skates. They stood and chatted and Henry tried out his Pennsylvania brand of German on them.

We'd not been on the ice an hour when snow began to fall. Huge white flakes like feathers settled on the bare trees and the gray roof tiles of the pavilion, touching it all with a silent beauty that made me forget for a moment the filth that choked the city outside the palace gates.

Their Majesties rose, accepted our bows once again, and then withdrew. One of the attendants called us to the pavilion as servants scuttled about setting low tables laden with a Korean feast. They laid thick bright cushions on the stone floor for us to sit on after we removed our skates and boots, then they placed charcoal burners here and there among us, which almost made us believe we were warm.

We ate thinly sliced broiled beef and spareribs pungent with sesame, garlic and soy sauce, and tiny fried fish cakes plus other items from the sea, some unrecognizable—it was just as well we didn't know what remarkable things we ate. Huge brass bowls of steaming white rice and others filled with hot chicken soup appeared before each of us and the servants crowded onto the tables dozens of small dishes of a variety of pickles and vegetables.

At that time Henry and I never ate with chopsticks at home and so we were not skilled in their use as we should have been although we did not drop them on the floor, I am thankful to say. As I glanced about I saw we were not the only ones whose hands were cramping. I *shall* master these stubborn sticks, I determined. Even though we lived in a growing Western community, it seemed to me we should at least know how to eat in the same manner as the natives.

———◼———

Henry worked as hard as a ditch digger at his school. He spent long hours with his students, not just in the classroom but also in talking with them at any time of day or night. I think the tenuous situation with the government pushed him to work with them while he could. He knew each boy's situation and who needed financial aid from the mission and who could make it on his own. He designed a system of work for extra pay as it went down hard with him to dole out money to any boy without the boy doing something in return.

Henry's goal was that each boy eventually would accept Christianity as the guiding light in his life. He was proud to be founder of the first Protestant Christian school in Korea and expected that school to affect the life of the nation. His efforts paid off. Long after dark one Sunday evening we heard a gentle tapping at the door just as we finished family prayers.

"Who could that be?" Henry muttered.

"Will you go and see," I asked, "while I put Alice to bed?"

Henry ambled toward to the door while I went into the nursery to ready Alice for sleep, no simple task. Whenever she knew it was time for sleep she wanted to socialize. We played games while she undressed, then I told her a story and gave her a drink of water. We said prayers together and I wished her goodnight four times before I could close the door for the night on our little chatterbox.

In the front room I was startled to see Henry in conversation with one of his students. I'd forgotten about the soft tap at the front door. I lingered to listen as they hadn't noticed me and my eavesdropping told me that Yong Byung, a second-year student, wanted to know more about Jesus. He came to ask questions of his teacher.

"But Honorable Teacher, how do you know that this man, Jesus, is God's son?"

"The Bible, this book I hold in my hand, tells us about His life and gives us His words. He often said that God, Jesus' Father and our Creator, sent Him to the world to bring God's love to all people. And we who are Christians believe that the Bible is true. We study and follow its teachings."

"I understand your custom of following the teachings of your Great Book, but I wonder how you, how anyone can be sure it speaks truth...there are so many great books in the world."

I slipped into our bedroom and with my head against the back of the chair I rocked to and fro to the cadence of their murmuring voices. The wonder of what was taking place washed over me like a wave of sea water on a sultry day. A Korean boy was risking everything to satisfy his curiosity about his foreign teacher's faith.

Which is why we are here, I thought. It is why we traveled so far and suffered through the wretched journey; why we left our homes, our families, why we shed tears and endure homesickness; why we do without the creature comforts so natural to life at home; why we insist on staying when our host country calls us dangerous and threatens us with harm or death if we propagate our faith here. All this so that Yong Byung can discover Jesus Christ and learn to walk in His light. It made sense and brought a measure of satisfaction although I felt like a bystander, an observer, not a participant.

What began that Sunday night continued each week. We came to expect the boy's gentle tap at the door after dark. His questions continued and we prayed for him each day as Henry gently taught him the Way.

Not everything about the school was clandestine and quiet. A major breakthrough delighted Henry beyond words. It all had to do with a name.

Henry had yearned at length for government approval and support for his school and knew that the best way for Korea to acknowledge it as an acceptable learning institution was for the president of the foreign office or, better yet, the king to visit the school and then suggest a name for it.

The president of the foreign office talked with Horace Underwood about his orphanage—which was really a school—and also called upon Mrs. Scranton to learn about her efforts with women and girls. Ever equal to any task, she served him cake and showed him magic lantern slides so he went away from there impressed and delighted.

"I've got to get that man to visit our school!" Henry fussed and fumed for days, trying to attract the government's attention for his boys. He sent his language teacher and helper plus one of his finest students to call on the foreign office president but the man was not at home. (He was taking a nap or gone off to drink tea with a friend, I suspected.)

Henry next sent a letter that the man deigned to answer. "I will come and visit your school within a few days," he wrote. But a month passed with no visit. Because Henry had met this official at Mrs. Scranton's magic lantern party, he felt bold enough to send another message.

Persistence wins because in February it happened! A Mr. Kim, foreign office secretary and interpreter, came to the school carrying a large sign board (five feet long by two feet wide, painted red, blue and gold) with the name suggested, he said, by the king and the president of the foreign office.

"Pai Jai Haktang," which means Hall for Rearing Useful Men. A lovely name. God knew Korea needed useful men and if anyone could produce them it was Henry Appenzeller. This I knew.

"This takes the negative questions away from our being here," Henry said. "No one can accuse us of being in opposition to the king or his government now that he has given his approval of our work by the bestowal of this name."

Prayers of thanksgiving were long and hearty that day.

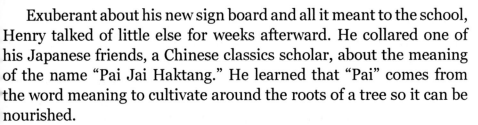

Exuberant about his new sign board and all it meant to the school, Henry talked of little else for weeks afterward. He collared one of his Japanese friends, a Chinese classics scholar, about the meaning of the name "Pai Jai Haktang." He learned that "Pai" comes from the word meaning to cultivate around the roots of a tree so it can be nourished.

The second word, "Jai," means material for building a house, and when speaking of persons it means those useful in a political sense. And "Haktang" is educational institution, so the idea that Henry's school was to be a Hall for Rearing Useful Men suggested that those who study there would contribute to the building of Korean society.

"The Korean government expects your school," said Henry's scholarly friend, "to raise useful persons."

"I hope," my husband replied, "to turn out men who shall be useful to the government and more especially to the people of Korea."

I heard Henry say it countless times: "I expect the graduates of PaiJai school will know and follow Christianity or my time is wasted."

Mrs. Scranton's school for girls also received its name from the government. "Ewha," it was called, which means Pear Blossom. Nice and feminine. Dr. Scranton's hospital? The Universal Relief Hospital. Will and his mother, like Henry, also received beautiful signboards from the government. Loulie was so proud that she, like my Henry, could talk of little else.

The hospital and the schools, along with their brilliantly colored sign boards also acquired ceremonial guards, a red-and-blue-clad soldier sent to each from the foreign office. The one at PaiJai followed Henry whenever he went out into the city and my husband enjoyed this thoroughly.

"The presence of the guard has a very good effect upon the school," he claimed. Not to mention how it turned heads when he walked about.

I knew he was thankful for the recognition and anxious to use this influence for the salvation of Koreans but it did tickle me to watch him march out through the compound gate with his guard clumping along behind. Henry went out soberly dressed in a black Western suit while his guard's bright and gauzy garments fluttered in the wind like a sword carrier from an opera.

Spring's arrival saw Henry planning a trip north to Pyengyang in company with a man in the customs service.

"One of the first foreigners to travel into interior Korea...just think!" he repeated until I wanted to scream. I fought hard to keep my feelings to myself for I felt as if he was abandoning me to sinister forces waiting to attack Alice and me, yet I was supposed to support him in every venture he saw fit to undertake in the name of God.

But whatever should I do while he was gone? I thought of a thousand things that could go wrong with me there in Seoul and with him wandering about that hostile country unprotected. Even his red-and-blue guard would stay at his post by the school. Had he already forgotten his government status as dangerous and undesirable?

I chewed raw the inside of my lower lip as Henry prattled on about his journey into the countryside of Korea, for I churned and boiled wanting in the worst way to throw things at him. But people like me didn't act like that, so I kept my eyes on the floor and my protests bottled up as I was taught a good wife should.

Chapter 13

The Reluctant Guardian

On Easter Horace Underwood and I decorated our Union Church meeting place with potted plants. He provided more muscle in moving the heavy greenery than artistic wisdom in placing them. We got on well, however, and I felt that the plants complemented the cut flowers—forsythia and azaleas—brought in by Mrs. Scranton and her friends. Loulie didn't feel well enough to help us.

Henry preached a pretty good message that day about how the resurrection will take place for each of us who follow the Lord. I felt, though, that he was a bit too argumentative and ignored the inspiration of the day when he stressed the importance of following Jesus to the neglect of the miracle of his resurrection, but no doubt God told him what to say so I kept my opinions to myself.

Perhaps my emotional state colored my attitude about Easter worship for I was troubled clear to the bottom of my soul. Abandoned, that's what I felt, but it didn't seem to matter to anyone but me. Henry left the next day for the interior with Mr. Hunt of the customs service, their destination being the large northern city of Pyengyang. I could hardly bear to see him go, but could do nothing about it.

I packed countless boxes of supplies for their journey and listed every item on sheets of paper. Food, fuel, utensils, clothing, bedding, toiletries, gifts—all snugly tucked in, awaiting the travelers' need. Henry and Hunt departed, self-sufficient and equipped against every exigency.

But what about Alice and me? Who would equip us against the filthy, hostile world outside our compound gate? Who would bolt the door against intruders? Who would set the stove damper each night so the fire wouldn't go out? Who would persuade the beggars and children to leave when they sneaked up and peered in our windows?

Of course I knew the answer to all these wailing questions...I, Ella Appenzeller, would do it. All of it. I dreaded that separation more than anything I had grappled with since we married.

Henry knew how I felt. He had to for I tried often to speak of it. He turned away from those attempts at conversation, however, unwilling to discuss my feelings and fears. He was so thrilled to embark on this pioneer mission jaunt that he could not bear to let Alice and me stand in his way.

And we didn't. I stood in the spring sunlight and waved him through the gate though I couldn't see him clearly through the tears.

The exasperating man returned finally after wandering for almost a month. My fickle heart spilled over with joy at the sight of him striding up the path toward our door. I ran out with Alice to meet him and it took me a moment to realize that she was dragging her feet.

"Come, darling," I cried, tugging at her hand.

"Mama?" she murmured, and then hid her face in my skirt.

"Look who's come!" I urged, but she wouldn't let go. Henry stopped in his tracks and called to her. "Alice?"

"Who is that nice man?" I asked her then. She lifted her curly head and studied the man standing before her. Tall and handsome but thinner than when he left, he wore a blue flannel shirt instead of the dark suit in which he always goes to school.

"Papa?" Alice wasn't sure but she thought, hoped, it was her wandering father come home at last.

Henry could wait no longer and scooped up his little girl, laughing and exclaiming how glad he was to see her. The sound of his voice and the twinkle of his eyes swept away her doubts and she hugged his neck with all her might. "Papa!" she cried, convinced at last of the identity of the strange-looking man who held her.

As soon as we moved indoors, Henry reached out and drew me close to Alice on his other arm, and himself. The three of us stood there for a moment, content and full of joy at being together again.

The insomnia that plagued me during Henry's absence disappeared instantly. I reported to him in full about the school, which he left under my supervision. How glad I was to be free of that, although it turned out I continued keeping the financial records because he insisted I was better at this than he, and he was right. We didn't talk about my feelings on his going. He did search my face for animosity, though, as he held me in his arms.

"How did you fare, dear Ella, while I was gone?"

"We managed just fine," I answered, and it sufficed that time—for both of us. I knew such separations would continue to be part of our missionary life. But lacking the resources to cope with his absences, I chose not to think about them at all.

Henry was thrilled with the mission board's approval (which came while he was gone) to build a proper brick school building for PaiJai. He created wonderful plans for the erection of the first such Western-style building in Korea and was so proud that our mission and no one else would be first.

He plunged back into his work while my mind turned again to reflect on how I suffered over his going on such a long trip away from Alice and me. Why did it upset me so? Why did I have trouble sleeping without him here? When Henry rode off with Mr. Hunt and their eight pack horses, Seoul turned into a nightmare for me, a sinister city filled with threats. Alice and I never walked out to South Gate even once although the spring weather normally would have drawn me there like a bee to a flower.

Loulie and I talked about my difficulty over tea one afternoon. "Ella, dear, have you prayed about this?" she asked after I told her of my fears and anger at being left alone. "Yes, I have," I answered through gritted teeth (not exactly true), "but what good does that do?"

I know I shocked her and, truth to tell, I had hoped for a less predictable response from my closest friend. Her suggestion regarding prayer sounded like something her mother-in-law might say to me.

Resentment. I pondered it for days. Was this my problem? Did I resent Henry's freedom to go adventuring, serene in the knowledge that all would be cared for until he returned?

If this was the case—and I suspected it was—then I surely required forgiveness for such wicked feelings. I knew my duty as wife and missionary but knowing duty and finding the heart to perform it were as different for me as rocks and eggs.

I frantically beseeched the Almighty to keep everyone from detecting my unworthy, unspiritual battles of the heart, sure in my soul that I deserved censure and ostracism for them. This was all I knew about such battles and my greatest concern, foolish me, was: what would people say?

Henry and Horace found us a summer place on a breezy bluff above the Han River three and a half miles out of the city in Mapo. In that large, rambling Korean-style house with courtyards and outbuildings, the Herons, Horace Underwood and we Appenzellers each had sleeping space plus a common living room. It was glorious! With the sky bright above us—the rainy season finally ended—we swam in the river or rowed about in small boats, played croquet, or called on other Westerners who also took summer places out there.

The Scrantons went to Chemulpo, taking rooms at a place called, oddly enough, Harry's Hotel. I believed Loulie and the doctor enjoyed a good rest, especially because the doctor's mother, Mrs. Scranton, elected to stay in Seoul. I knew it benefitted them to be without her that summer— it surely did me.

Henry rode into Seoul a couple of times each week to check on the construction of his beloved school building. He was so proud of their progress and delighted that the mission gained prestige by being viewed as an aid to Korean development. Of course we both wanted most of all that Korean people come to faith, the reason behind all our activities, and we expected the Lord to honor it all with conversions in His own good time.

Which He did. On July 24th Henry baptized Pak Choong Sang, one of his PaiJai students who learned about Christianity in Japan.

"I give him entirely into the Lord's hands," Henry told me as he prepared for the baptism, "because then only is he safe."

I shuddered to think what a risk Pak took by openly declaring his Christian faith in the face of a government that forbade such action.

Meanwhile, mail brought us word that Bishop and Mrs. H.W. Warren would visit Korea in the fall. As I sat by the river with Alice napping on a quilt beside me, I couldn't even stir up a good worry about what their visit would mean, for I was too relaxed and comfortable. We can deal with that when we return to Seoul, I told the birds that twittered among the leaves overhead.

On one of his trips into the city, Henry laid the cornerstone for the new school building. "Hayakawa and Yoshizawa will be there with me," he said as he mounted his pony. These were his Japanese Christian friends. "And I shall ask Mrs. Scranton to place the Bible into the stone during the ceremony."

It is nice for Henry, I decided as I waved goodbye, that Mrs. Scranton will be there for his little event because he admires her spiritual and ministerial gifts so lavishly. I was content to enjoy my peace and comfort beside the river.

Chapter 14

Increasing Anxiety

Bishop Warren and his party arrived in Korea in September. He and his wife stayed with us while Loulie made space for their son. Mrs. Miller, their traveling companion, lodged with Mrs. Scranton. We all felt flustered and flurried to be entertaining anyone, let alone a bishop and his entourage. All of a sudden we saw our own accommodations with wiser eyes; that which seemed quite satisfactory—pretty, even— suddenly appeared shabby and pathetic compared to what we knew our visitors had come from back home.

I walked around the house twitching at curtains and staring at the smoke-smudged corners, wondering if Mrs. Warren considered us hopeless drudges. I looked at my clothes—good gracious! Why had I settled for such dreary fabrics, all in the name of practicality? She wore such lovely, light-colored, lace-trimmed gowns. She was old enough to be my mother and yet I felt like an ancient crone when we sat together in the same room. Their visit cannot end too soon for me, I huffed.

The bishop's days with us were jammed with meetings and events. I listed them in my diary.

September 11—Loulie's new baby, Katherine, received baptism at the hands of Bishop Warren during worship this morning.

September 12—There was a mission meeting all day and then dinner at the Foreign Office in honor of the king's 36th birthday. The Warrens were included in our invitation. Mrs. Warren wore a pale yellow silk gown dripping with ecru lace that left me paralyzed with envy. Henry and I looked pathetic: he with his too-big shirt collar and me in serviceable, boring brown.

September 13—There were more mission meetings and lengthy discussion about the work. Mrs. Scranton held a reception in the evening. It rained.

September 14—Henry took guests on a tour of Seoul: an old palace, East Gate, and a temple. They did not insist that I go along. In the afternoon were opening exercises in PaiJai's new building. Horace Underwood spoke in Korean. There is a prayer meeting with Bishop this evening...a long day.

September 15—Henry accompanied the Bishop and his party back to Chemulpo where they will board a ship for China. I tackled guest laundry and sent Granny to market to re-supply our kitchen.

My energy disappeared. Odd how sitting in hours-long meetings, lingering at the dining table or in the parlor chatting with guests can tire one so. We were highly honored to be visited by a bishop but I was glad to see them go. I checked in the mirror to see if my eyes had turned permanently green from all my envious thoughts about Mrs. Warren's wardrobe. Fortunately, they were the same brown as before; unfortunately, so were my clothes.

New missionaries, two women, arrived before we recovered from the Bishop's visit and stayed with us until suitable housing was found for them. Even though Henry and I were weary, I wanted us to make Metta Howard and Louisa Rockwiler feel welcome for I remembered all the hospitality people expended on our account before we finally found a home of our own.

Mrs. Scranton, however, took upon herself responsibility for the newcomers. She assumed that the two women were entrusted to her care. She called for them each morning with the day meticulously planned, so my hostessing was limited to meals and clean clothing. She didn't appear to notice that I felt displaced and badly done by.

Mrs. Scranton, I presumed in those days, was insensitive and careless about the feelings of others, especially mine.

Christmas Day was good that year, clouded only slightly by my touch of homesickness, which didn't last long. Alice enjoyed having playmates with whom she unpacked her stocking. Two boys from the school were working for us and so shared our Christmas as well. Henry told them the story of Jesus' birth and they drank it in, never having heard such a tale before.

And to cap off a perfect holiday in my husband's estimation, the dear man preached in Korean for the first time that afternoon. He worked for hours with a Korean helper, getting the grammar and thought patterns just so. Of course, Horace Underwood preached first, but Henry found a historical first to tag his effort with anyway.

"The first sermon preached in this country by someone from our mission," he called it, and seemed content that this was so.

In January crushing news came in a letter from home, my first family loss. My Aunt Sarah, Mother's younger sister and a favorite of mine, had died. The shock and pain almost overwhelmed me for I never knew she was ill and even after reading the letter I still didn't know what ailment carried her off—Mother forgot to say—and the awful letter reached me weeks after such a terrible thing took place.

I sobbed and stormed into my pillow, thinking that as I was living out my days in a normal fashion, doing my work, playing with my child, entertaining guests and trying to be a good wife, all the while my dear Aunt Sarah sickened, died, was buried and mourned by everyone else in the family, but I was not a part of any of it. I didn't even know it was happening.

Lord, You claim Your yoke is easy and Your burden is light, I railed at Him. Right now I do not find it so.

One windy March day, Henry and I left the compound and went out into the city to see the royal procession headed toward the kings' tombs to offer sacrifices and honor their dead. The colors of the banners and royal clothing were wondrous to see, I thought, for I looked with eyes too long focused on mud, garbage and gray thatched roofs. The red, blue, yellow, purple and green glowed against the dinginess that surrounded us.

We stood close to the palace gate, which resembled South Gate near our home. While waiting, Henry amused himself eavesdropping on comments made by the milling Korean crowd, comments about our faces, our dress and the country from which we come. Koreans looked upon us as "outside persons" (a literal translation of the Korean phrase) with whom they have no relationship whatsoever, and so they talked about us as if we were not there, assuming that we could not comprehend what they said.

Consequently, the length of our noses, the color of our eyes, and my brazenness at coming out of the house with my husband were discussed at length. Some of the talk, however, was positive. One noble *yangban*, whose flushed face and slurred speech testified to his celebrating the day with his wine bottle, waxed eloquent about the American lead pencil. This wonderful invention, he declared, did away with the necessity for carrying about the ink stone, brush and water dropper that equipped the writer of Oriental characters.

After listening to the white-clad gentleman praise the pencil for a while, Harry then muttered in my ear, "Wonder what he would say about fountain pens?"

That same spring our little foreign community welcomed a new missionary. Lillias Horton, M.D., came to help in the hospital and to provide medical care for Queen Min and her palace women. The Herons were so excited by her arrival that they gave a most lavish tea (well, lavish for those times) and invited us all.

Miss Horton was not young, late thirties I guessed, but she was such a tiny thing that she always seemed youthful. I had not thought about Horace Underwood and Miss Horton becoming interested in each other—she was several years his senior, after all—until I caught a glimpse of his face as he gazed at her during the Herons' party. He looked besotted with the new doctor. Wouldn't that be interesting, I crowed.

Just a few days after the welcome tea, Horace and Henry departed for a journey into the Korean countryside; 1,500 miles they planned to travel and God alone knew when they would return. Again, I mourned my aloneness, but they were like two boys, shouting and laughing as they rode out through the gate followed by a string of pack animals. They did not seem to sense or care that I didn't share their joy over the venture.

Horace did not let on, to us at least, if he minded leaving for such a lengthy journey now that the dainty doctor had intruded upon his horizon. "Has Horace said anything to you about being interested in Lillias Horton?" I asked Henry.

"What? The new doctor and Horace? Whatever gave you that idea?" He obviously knew nothing and noticed nothing. We'll wait and see, I thought, sure that my instincts were correct.

———————■———————

More new missionaries, the Ohlingers, upon their arrival tried to study Korean and work in PaiJai at the same time. So much to do. By then it looked as if the work of treasurer and bookkeeper was mine permanently. I could do it at home, which pleased me, but at the same time I allowed Henry to persuade me to teach English to his boys, which did not please me. I was not a born teacher like my husband so I dragged myself to each session and then when the hour was finished, I was more eager (if possible) than my pupils to quit the classroom.

Now that spring had finally come, I kidnapped Alice from the servants after class and we walked out to South Gate for a look at the blue sky and the circling mountains. The gate guards welcomed us and placed straw mats on the stone steps for us to sit on when they saw us coming. Alice even allowed them to lift her up in their arms and walk about for a time. She learned Korean words from them, which pleased her father no end. Our times at the gate were for me like a visit with an old friend.

My two big boys, solemn-faced, returned the first week in May, their journey cut short by an edict from the king, no less. He ordered them to stop disseminating Christianity because "it is objectionable to the government of Korea and not authorized by the treaty. I demand that it shall cease."

It seemed that the Catholics had again displeased the king and his company by building a church in a prominent location near West Gate, which overlooked the palace, although Korean culture forbade anything to stand higher than royalty. Rather than bow to royal disapproval, however, the Catholics stubbornly continued. This stubbornness jeopardized all of us and Henry was most upset with the Catholics, for whom he held small regard in any case.

So we were reminded once again that we perched on a political powder keg, a fact that frayed the nerves and sapped the appetite although both Henry and Horace insisted we were in no personal danger. All religious meetings, however, were suspended for the time being.

Returning from class one day I found Granny (with Alice riding on her back in good Korean style) whispering with the gateman. They broke off their conversation when they saw me and I didn't think much about it at first.

"Shall you and I go for a walk?" I said to Alice in English.

"Do not go out, Honorable Wife." The gateman couldn't understand my English but he knew our normal habit after my class.

"Why? What's the matter?" I asked him.

Both he and Granny looked at the ground, avoiding my eyes, but both urged me to stay within the compound. "Big problems," was all they would tell me. By then Alice wanted to swing beneath the big tree near the Scranton's so I let it go, although a cold chill crept down my spine. Maybe, I speculated, the "big problems" had to do with the king's difficulties with the Catholics.

Then, not too many days afterward, when green leaves and grass were finally overcoming the mud, people began rioting in the streets in protest against foreigners, shouting, screaming, flailing mindlessly with sticks. Some Koreans were caught in the violence and lost their lives. Henry insisted that Alice and I stay indoors but refused to discuss the cause of the disturbance. "It's too horrible to talk about," was all he would tell me. Irritated because of his apparent lack of trust, at the same time I knew his refusal grew out of love and his desire to protect me. But his tendency to clam up and refuse to talk about problems made me angry because not knowing made me afraid. I felt shut off from him and from understanding what threatened us while the trouble, whatever it was, lurked all around like a child's monsters that people the dark. More to the point, I asked, must I spend the rest of my days with ice in my stomach and panic squeezing the heart out of me? Does anyone care? Should we pack our cases? There were no answers, only questions.

"Baby killers!" That's what they were calling foreigners in Seoul, Henry finally told me, but not before I took him to the front window and pointed at our little porch.

"Do you remember what you promised me right out there?" I prodded. "You said we would always talk things out and not hide them. Don't you remember the months of misery you put me through when you wouldn't talk? How we hurt and suffered because we couldn't stay in Korea? How much I needed...."

"Yes, Ella, I remember, and I'm sorry. I'll talk!" He threw up his hands in surrender and that's when he told me that the people of Seoul believed we Americans were killing babies. "They think we butcher children at the hospital, that children are fattened in the orphanage for unspeakable sexual reasons, that our tinned milk comes from Korean women mutilated at the hospital." He was right. Such ideas were unspeakable, but he was wrong to keep it all from me for not knowing only made it worse.

One bright spot shone out in those days when Marines from American ships in Chemulpo arrived to protect the legation from rioters. I thanked God we lived so close by and could benefit from their presence. Then one day shortly after the Marines arrived Granny returned from South Gate Market.

"What did you see? What are they saying?" I queried her.

She shook her head and kept her eyes on the floor as she scuttled toward the kitchen. "Stay in the house," was all she would say. Is she in jeopardy because she works for the dreadful foreigners, I wondered.

Henry decided to cancel his trip south, something he'd planned since his and Horace's abortive venture at the beginning of all this. He also dismissed PaiJai classes. Drs. Scranton, Heron and Horton, however, went to the hospital each day. Loulie told me that Horace Underwood accompanied Lillias on horseback after her sedan chair was attacked by a mob. The rioters let her slip through their grasping hands but threatened injury and death to her bearers if they continued serving the Westerners.

The atmosphere of our home during those terrible days pulsated with fear and uncertainty as Henry and I pondered what to do. Little Alice soaked it all up like a blotter and would not turn loose of my skirts. Each move I made, each task I attempted was done with my curly-headed baby knotting her fingers in my clothes or, if she could manage it, with her arms clamped round my neck. I wanted to scream. Henry did, too, I'm sure, but with his mouth closed as tightly as mine, he walked up and down in the house like a jungle beast caged in a zoo.

Finally the king broke the tension before rioters breached our walls and came after us. With amazing wisdom he decreed that any missing children should be reported to the authorities and false reports against foreigners must cease. Those fostering the rumors would be arrested. By these edicts he restored a measure of reason to the crazed populace of Seoul.

The city grew quiet. Relief flooded in and we began to breathe again. I still found it most disturbing to live among people so confused by our foreignness that they believed us capable of the despicable things that ignited the fracas, which I shall never forget. I mulled it over constantly. Just when we believed the barriers between us were melting, they turned on us. Why? What did we do?

While I fumed over unanswerable questions, Henry decreed that we needed a holiday. "Ella, how would you like to go to Nagasaki in Japan? Let's leave Korea entirely for several weeks." What an incredible idea! I packed almost before he finished the question and boarded the ship a few days later without a qualm. Even seasickness

would be an improvement over rioting Koreans filled with hate
against us.

Chapter 15

Head-On With Mrs. Scranton

We were guests again but, believe me, I didn't mind. I loved it, in fact: no responsibility, no riots, meals planned and prepared but not by me, and long warm days through which I could read, sleep, walk, picnic...or sit and do nothing if I chose.

The Japanese streets were clean. I could not help comparing them to what I'd left in Seoul. And the people! If they felt curious about us foreigners, they did not reveal it like the Koreans did. So I relaxed and enjoyed the surface anonymity of Nagasaki. Both Henry and I gained a pound or two in our indolence.

"Ella, let me take a look at the PaiJai ledger." Henry strode into our bedroom early one morning before I'd even gotten up.

"Ledger?" I replied stupidly. Then I laughed as I stretched my arms over my head. "They're in Seoul, darling. Gathering dust back home." This fact delighted me all out of proportion to its significance.

"You didn't bring them? Not even one?" Now whose turn was it to be stupid? I persuaded him to come to the bed and kiss me, hoping to distract his attention from my indolence. It worked.

So Henry wrote letters, reams of them, although none found us there in response. What freedom, what decadent pleasure. Alice felt it, too, although she grew cross when the Japanese servants didn't understand her Korean. She was too young to sort out differences of nationality or even to know she spoke two languages, so she couldn't comprehend why her store of words didn't provoke the same action as it did at home.

So much freedom must have fostered rebellion in me for in defiance of all that was sensible, I had a white shirtwaist made. I justified it in my thinking by saying of course I would wear it with dark skirts. But still stinging from the bishop's wife's visit I had it trimmed with lace, awfully narrow but it boasted deep, snug cuffs on the sleeves, just like the ones I saw in an American magazine left lying on a chair in the house in which we stayed.

God will forgive me, I presumed, for giving in to my yearning for something pretty to wear. Part of me wondered just how much it mattered to Him one way or the other anyway.

Our summer idyll ended too soon. We sloshed back across the straits and returned to Seoul. No sooner did we walk into our house and unpack than Henry rode off on another of his beloved journeys into inland Korea.

"A 700-mile horseback ride," he called it for anyone who would listen. Off to the Chinese border this time, evangelizing when he could even though the law prohibited such behavior, and contacting the scattered Christian believers he knew lived in the towns and villages along his path.

"Will Horace go with you?" I probably sounded petulant as I questioned Henry about his horseback ride. Unwell and weary, my vacation benefits vanished; again I struggled to adjust to another absence.

"Oh, no, he's not." Henry sounded a bit whiny himself. "He's courting Lilias, you know. Too busy." Horace's constant attendance at the doctor's side kept him away from his friend. Prayer meetings, horseback rides, all social gatherings saw them together.

"I think it's quite charming," I said. "They'll announce their engagement soon, you know."

But the issues in the Appenzeller home had nothing to do with courtship and newborn love. I was upset with Henry's defection for the long weeks ahead, and he knew it. He knew I was against his going but that knowledge didn't faze him.

"I know you don't feel well, Ella." At least he admitted that much. "But Scranton's good care is making a difference. You're improving every day!"

His hopeful heartiness made me want to scream. He seemed to me like a child bent on having his own way no matter what. As we talked I struggled to keep my emotions under control and to be a proper wife and in so doing I felt my insides twist into knots while my hands shook like a grandmother's.

"Yes, I am some better, but still, just living is more of a task than I am equal to and when you're gone I have no one to depend on, no other strength to draw on. Right now I feel as if I cannot cope with everything on my own. I need you, Henry! Can't you see that?"

So much for propriety, I thought, as I listened to my self-pity bounce off the white ceiling of our bedroom. What a disappointment I must have been to my poor husband.

"Now, now, Ella." He clumsily patted my shoulder but could not look into my eyes, so there we stood with the boxes and bundles of his supplies strewn across the floor, comrades of Henry's yearning to be gone and accusers of my inability to tolerate that yearning.

"Papa!" Alice raced to Henry who scooped her up and tossed her high toward the rafters, relieved, it seemed to me, by the diversion. I turned and brushed away my tears for I did not want anyone to see how inadequate I was.

Henry strode to the front door with Alice over his shoulder. "Come and carry out the baggage," he called to the men waiting with the horses outside. "Load up. We must be going."

The men removed all the bundles from the house and as they milled about in the yard loading the patient horses, my husband turned to me with Alice still in his arms.

"I'm sorry, Ella, that you feel this way. I shall pray every day that the Lord will protect you, will heal you and will help you see that my going is in response to His direction. This is why we are here in Korea. I must go. I can't not go, don't you see?"

He laid his free hand on my upper arm and started to draw me to him so the three of us could share one last embrace.

"Am I to assume, then," I said, stiff and unyielding, "that the Lord is saying it is proper to sacrifice your wife's health and well-being on the altar of your missionary call?"

Henry stared at me for a moment as my words cut their way into his heart. His grip tightened as if in a spasm of pain. Then he leaned forward and kissed my forehead before he removed his hand from my arm. He closed his eyes and squeezed Alice tightly in both arms.

"Goodbye, my baby," he said to her. "Be good, and take care of Mama."

He turned to go. Alice scampered after him to see the horses one more time. I turned away from the door and into the bedroom where I laid down on the white covers, sick in body and in heart.

November came with its feeble sunlight. No word from Henry but then I didn't expect any. The postal service in those days wobbled between sporadic and non-existent. My heart was as gray as the roof tiles on our house.

One afternoon while I sat with Loulie, drinking tea, Mrs. Scranton sailed in, hair knotted back and formidable bosom cutting a path before her like the prow of a ship. As usual, her presence made me feel uneasy, anxious somehow, like a child caught in some unacceptable behavior. Loulie's cook called her to the kitchen to deal with a vendor at the back door. As soon as she left, Mrs. Scranton turned to me.

"You don't like me very much, do you?"

"Why, I don't know what you...." I gulped mid-sentence and stared at the woman seated across from me. Straight-backed, hands quiet in her lap, she gazed back at me, neither smiling nor frowning, just waiting, I think, for my initial fluster to pass.

"Why do you ask me that, Mrs. Scranton?" I said finally.

"Perhaps you know that I am a very direct person," she replied "and I am troubled that after these several years of our close association you still hold yourself aloof from me. I feel as if you avoid me and I don't understand why. The only way I know to deal with the problem is head on, which is why I am asking you such a question."

Unlike the calm, contained, and formidable Mrs. Scranton, my clammy hands were twisting my handkerchief into a pathetic shred as I sat there under her scrutiny. She was right. I didn't much like her but that isn't something one says to another person, even if it is true. How should I reply to her? My first reaction—Lord forgive me—was to lie, to say that I didn't know what she was talking about. Of course I liked her. We were co-workers in the Lord's vineyard. He commanded us to love one another and so we do...don't we?

"It isn't so much a matter of dislike, Mrs. Scranton, although, come to think of it, it seems to be the outcome." I astonished myself when I opened my mouth at last to respond. I began in spite of myself to tell her the truth about my feelings, honestly and candidly.

"Around you I feel so...inadequate, I think is the word. Yes, that's it. My husband admires you so; he sings your praises constantly, about how hard you work and how effective you are as a missionary."

Looking back, my response to Mrs. Scranton's shocking question still astounds me. Where did such forthrightness come from? It felt like river ice cracking and breaking loose in early spring. Painful release, but release just the same. Without question she deserved credit for initiating the encounter, although I benefitted in ways I'm finally beginning to understand.

"That's all very nice, I'm sure," she retorted, "but why does my doing my job make you treat me as if I were a, a ...cholera patient?"

"I didn't mean to treat you any way. I guess I only intended to stay out of your way."

"Well, my dear, you certainly succeeded in that. We have exchanged greetings or discussed the weather a maximum of three times since you and I arrived in Seoul and I am determined to find out why. As God knows my heart, I wish you no ill and I wonder why the same is not true for you as regards me."

She maintained her calm appearance as she finished speaking but I did notice the knuckles on her clasped hands were white. I learned at that moment that the invincible Mrs. Scranton endured emotions along with us lesser mortals.

"As I said, Mrs. Scranton, for reasons beyond my control and that I don't understand, I feel inadequate and worthless somehow when I compare my life to yours. All the qualities Henry finds so admirable in you are completely lacking in me. I don't enjoy teaching; you have founded a girls' school. My health has deteriorated since we came to Korea; you appear robust to the point where you took no holiday last summer. You have established a home, extended hospitality to visitors and Koreans alike plus doing your mission work, all on your own without a husband's strength, while I..."

Here, predictably, I burst into tears. My distress over Henry's absence smashed holes in my flimsy self-control. Mrs. Scranton jumped to her feet and dragged her chair up close to mine.

"My dear child, oh, my dear," she murmured, and drew me into her arms. Unable to continue, I sobbed out my pain on her shoulder, soaking her dress and my poor twisted handkerchief.

"Something else is wrong, isn't it, besides misunderstanding between you and me? Do you want to talk about it? Has it to do with Henry's travel into the interior?"

Of course I told her. She'd put her finger right on the sore spot and I could not resist such warmth, such caring, even from this unexpected source. I told her about the bitter parting between Henry and me on the day he left against my will. I told her what a struggle it was for me to survive when he takes such journeys and how very un-Christlike were my feelings about his going.

Finally my flow of tears and words dried up. I felt exhausted, as if I had gardened all day in the sun; drained energy was a major symptom of my illness. "And so you see, Mrs. Scranton, although I have not always recognized it myself, my problems have less to do with you as a person than with the way your abilities show up my inadequacies."

"Nonsense!" she sniffed. Then she looked at me and gentled her tone. "I mean for you to call yourself inadequate is nonsense. And it is nonsense to compare yourself to me because I am old enough to be your mother and because of those additional years, my experiences are more numerous than yours. Please be yourself...and be a friend to me, as I want to be one to you."

"And as I'm in this far, I shall plunge on." She drew a deep breath and the frown lines between her eyebrows deepened slightly. "You,

my dear Ella, are so very concerned about appearances. You wonder
if you are behaving as you are expected to as a missionary wife. You
worry about what people think of you. You seem to gather your
directions, your marching orders from those around you." Tears
welled up again, this time pushed by anger at her sharp words, so I
kept silent, eyes on the floor.

"It's far more important, girl, to discover what God thinks of you."

Then my temper erupted, I'm afraid. "God evidently doesn't think
much of me at all," I sputtered.

"And how much do you think of Him?"

"Why, I...." Good grief, the woman never quit. But I was stuck.
God wasn't on my mind much at all, even during family prayers or
when Henry preached.

Mrs. Scranton gave a small triumphant nod, which irritated me
severely, but this she ignored as she continued. "You grew up in a
fine Christian home, did you not?" I nodded. She was right again. Of
course.

"But you see, Ella, all that fine teaching does not form a personal
relationship between you and God until you invite Him to take charge
of your life."

"But I thought Christians are...Christians. They belong to God
because they do right and go to church and..."

"No, no, not at all!" she interrupted.

"We're Christians because we accept Jesus as Savior and give
control of our lives to Him. We learn what pleases Him, what He
wants us to be, where He wants us to go."

"How do...?"

Again interrupting she leapt from her chair, frowning at the gold
watch pinned to her bosom. "Ah," she said, "you must excuse me. My
dinner guests will arrive within the hour and I have to check on the
cook's preparations."

She gave my shoulder an absent-minded pat as she started for
the door but then she checked herself, turned and looked straight
into my eyes. "Your good husband loves you very much," she said.
"Whenever we are together for any reason he speaks of you fondly and
frequently. But he is a man driven by his call to mission in Korea, by

his pioneering sense, by his hunger to introduce Koreans to the Lord Jesus. Unfortunately, such a man sometimes has trouble stretching himself around all his commitments and it is usually his wife who suffers. I shall pray for you, my dear, asking God to help you bear the pain of sharing the man you love with his life's calling."

I opened my mouth to respond to this very important thing she had just said but before I drew breath she was gone.

"I'm going, Loulie," I called toward the kitchen door.

"Oh, Ella, I'm so sorry to neglect you...one thing and another came up out here. Did you have a nice visit with Mother Scranton?" She giggled at that, knowing how I felt about her mother-in-law.

"Better than average," I replied, not quite believing what I heard myself saying, "much better than average."

Chapter 16

Heart-to-Heart With Mrs. Scranton

Henry returned at last, thin, needing a haircut, looking more than a month older, which is how long he was gone. Perhaps rest and good food will erase the dark shadows under his eyes, I thought, knowing that a good talk with me would help, too.

"Henry, could we walk out to South Gate tomorrow afternoon?" I asked him as soon as he'd greeted all those who came to welcome him back. "We haven't gone there together for so long."

He studied my face, searching for signals. For a month the poor man had carried the misery of our parting like a knife wound in his vitals and it showed on his face. I suspected I looked equally awful.

"I have some things I want to tell you," I said as gently as I knew how, trying to let him know that healing was on the way.

"Sounds good to me," he said, with nary a glance at his unanswered mail or the big basket that contained his translation work, which let me know that our difficulty was uppermost in his thinking as well as mine.

So walk out we did, to our dear old gate, which guarded us as faithfully as it did the city. The late afternoon light warmed her back (I always think of South Gate as facing inward toward Seoul, with her back turned to the rest of the world, rather like Korea, the Hermit Nation, has done for all these centuries) as the sun dropped toward the horizon, preparing to leave us all to the mercy of the winter chill.

We walked through the gate and up the slope toward the pine trees where Henry gave me my pearl ring. Each of us took a deep breath.

"Henry..."

"Ella..."

We stopped, turned and faced each other with our mouths aja
and lungs full of air with which to explain, apologize, and probabl
to justify. The air stayed in our lungs a moment longer as I searched
Henry's eyes, and he mine. I broke first and breathed out with a wail
throwing my arms around his neck with its too-big shirt collar. He
bent his knees just a bit, encircled my waist with his strong arms
picked me up and whirled me around among the gnarled old trees a
we both laughed until the tears poured down our faces.

"You are better, Ella, aren't you." He stated it rather than asked.

"Do you mean physically, or emotionally?"

"Both, I guess."

"So do I. Yes, I am better, and that is why I asked you to come ou
here with me. I want to tell you all about it...about how sorry I am...."

"Hush, dear," he laid his fingers on my lips, the healing laughte
still alive in his eyes. "Both of us were wrong and both of us are sorry
Let's go on from there."

So I told him of my encounter with Mrs. Scranton, everything tha
was said between us and about the fledgling relationship building
between God and me. My eyes misted up a bit at the part where she
said I must share my husband with his mission call, which was stil
not an easy thing to swallow.

Henry bowed his head at that and rubbed his eyebrows with his
left hand, and then he hunkered down just as Koreans do when they
are talking together, or thinking, or waiting. He absently picked up a
few pine needles and began laying them in the shape of a fan on the
ground. I sat down close beside him, tucking my skirt in tight agains
the chill.

"Mrs. Scranton is right," I said, "and I want to learn to be all
should be in the face of what you must do...of what you are, really."

"Yes, I guess she is right, but I never thought obeying God would
mean trouble and pain between you and me. Is that the way it has to
be?"

I wish I could say we solved this thorny issue once and for all ou
there beyond South Gate, but we didn't. We talked about it for more

than an hour, Harry folded down in his "Korean Uncle" pose and me facing him wrapped in my warm shawl.

We didn't solve anything with flashes of heavenly insight but I had a feeling buried away inside me that there was a solution, or at least a help for it although what that might be was still beyond me. I wanted help. I wanted a solution more than I could say, and though I didn't fully comprehend it then, the wanting made the finding so much easier.

On New Year's Day we missionary ladies (at the instigation of the men, of course) gave a reception, not only for the foreign community but for Korean officials as well. New Year's is a most important holiday for Oriental people, so Henry thought it an auspicious time to invite Korean friends and acquaintances to our home.

Everything went well. The refreshments came from a variety of kitchens and were well received. Although it is commonly said amongst us that Koreans do not like sweets, an astounding number of tarts, cakes and cookies disappeared down Korean throats before the end of the day.

At our house we observed the local custom of taking off shoes at the door and almost everyone followed that custom. Oddly enough, a minor official from the Foreign Office tromped on into the house in his shoes—having heard, I am sure, that Westerners do not behave as Koreans do—but one of his superiors soon set him straight, backing him out the door to leave his shoes. Funny he didn't notice all the other shoes on the porch. He had to step on at least 10 pairs to enter our parlor.

The Korean guests came en masse and therefore left in a body, which made it nice for Henry. A number of our other friends had not talked with him since his last country trip, so after the Korean guests took their leave, people pelted my husband with questions about what he had discovered on his journey. How proud he was to be able to speak of the growing number of Christian believers who came to him for baptism and instruction. And the believers were created, in the most part, by the courageous ministry of faithful Korean colporteurs who trekked across the countryside with Bibles to sell and hearts full of evangelistic fervor.

Capping the event and upstaging all else, Horace and Lillias announced their engagement at the New Year's reception. They came in radiating the sparkle and glow that had shone about them for a number of weeks. As soon as the Korean guests left, Horace worked his way to the center of the room with Lillias on his arm, but couldn't gain the attention of the crowd for a time because everyone was listening to Henry's description of his trip. Horace murmured something in Lillias' ear and they went to the table for more tea. Finally he couldn't stand it any longer.

"Appie," he boomed, "do you mind if I interrupt you for a moment?"

Henry looked across at his friend and chuckled. "Undie, old boy, I suspect it would make not the least bit of difference if I did mind. Why don't you go ahead?"

Horace looked down at the dainty little doctor clinging to his arm, aware he had our attention. She beamed back at him, her "Captain," she called him, and nodded.

"Ladies and gentlemen, dear friends all," he began, his voice penetrating to every corner of the room. "Dr. Lillias Horton has consented to become my bride so I am happy to announce our engagement. You all are invited to our wedding which will be held March 13, here in Seoul."

Cheers and applause erupted. The men pounded Horace on the back saying predictable things about his finally being caught, while women cooed and hugged Lillias with delight and good wishes. I'm afraid the spreading of the gospel was forgotten for a while as friends and neighbors shared the happiness of the engagement of two young people. For a few moments it didn't seem as if we were gathered in an Oriental city half a world away from home. But, in another sense, to us this Oriental city grew to be more homelike as the months and years turned through their cycles.

Horace and his Lillias married in March, as they planned. Queen Min, with whom Lillias was by then acquainted both professionally and socially, sent as a gift a long train of little pack horses bearing a million cash coins.

What a sight and sound that created! We heard the gongs and the drums early in the morning of the 13th, and men shouting, "Make way! Make way!"

We dashed to the gate with the servants at our heels. PaiJai boys perched on the wall, chattering with excitement as the brilliantly clad palace guards strutted along our little street preceding the long line of gray and brown ponies each bearing two huge wicker baskets filled with strings of cash. Each Korean coin had a square hole in its center and when they were counted, they were strung together a thousand per string, only Queen Min, in honor of the occasion, had her gift to Horace and Lillias strung on red silk cords. Befuddled by the excitement I failed to count the number of ponies that trotted by our gate but I know there were far more than the dozen or so that Henry hired when he brought mission money from Chemulpo.

Queen Min's gift, however, was not the most remarkable feature of that most remarkable wedding. The day following the ceremony, against the advice of Henry and everyone else, Horace and his bride set off on a 1,000-mile honeymoon journey from Seoul up north to the Yalu River and back. They planned to visit groups of believers and baptize those who were ready as well as see the sights of Korea along the way.

Lillias rode in a sedan chair that was nothing more than a box resting on two long poles borne by Koreans who trotted up hill and down, jostling their unfortunate passenger at every step. Knowing how she rode horseback here in town, as they moved off on their journey I wondered how she would take to such an arrangement.

By traveling out into the country with Horace, Lillias did something no other foreign woman had yet attempted. Part of me envied her and part of me shuddered, glad I didn't have to learn about marriage in such an environment.

Come April I was pregnant again. I told Henry when he returned from another country trip, south this time with "Brother Ohlinger," as he called him. He was pleased about the baby and hoped for a son. I did not feel so well. Meanwhile, the Foreign Minister refused Henry permission for any more country travel unless he promised to refrain from preaching and baptizing. He was crushed.

In June we took a month's holiday in a rented house in Chemulpo. Dr. Scranton recommended this to Henry as a possible remedy for my chronic tiredness and nausea. The sea air and the change of surroundings pleased and benefited me, to be sure, but too soon back in the heat and stench of Seoul wiped out the benefits within 24 hours. Even Henry said it was awful. Ever the scholar, he called it "an Augean stable."

Rainy season flushed out some of the filth of Seoul that summer. Heat and humidity still oppressed us, though, and my strength was non-existent. I struggled to complete the school accounts for the final weeks of the term. Dear Henry carried on, eternally encouraged by every expression by Koreans of interest in Christianity while I dreamed of the green hills of home. But the heat eased at last and I felt better. We were learning that after the middle of August, although temperatures remained high, humidity subsided and the air freshened almost like autumn. Something to look forward to.

When that happened I found I could get out the PaiJai books and catch up on my work in preparation for the return of the students. Henry liked all things in readiness at the first, and I wanted to please him. Perhaps too I was learning that God had tailored this task especially for me, something He wanted me to contribute.

So that late August morning I was scratching away at the dining table with bills and vouchers and account books spread all around me when Mrs. Scranton appeared at the front door. I can't truly say I grew all rosy with excitement whenever she appeared—after all, she was still the same formidable woman she always was, plus she knew more about my shortcomings than anyone outside my husband— but I didn't run for cover either. Over the months since our weepy conversation in Loulie's parlor, we managed to enjoy several pleasant, albeit innocuous talks.

I welcomed her easily. "Mrs. Scranton. How nice of you to come here. I'm working on school accounts and need a break. May I get you some tea?"

"Thank you, Ella, dear. That would be nice. My throat is dry."

I told Granny to bring us tea and *chami*, an odd yellow melon that grows in Korea.

"How are you feeling, Ella?" she began as soon as she was seated.

"I'm much better, Mrs. Scranton. The weather is more pleasant and I think I am, too. Our new little one," I gestured toward the bulge in the front of my dress, "slows me down some, but it's for a good cause, so I shan't complain."

"Henry must be terribly pleased."

"Yes. He hopes for a son this time, of course, but Alice could not ask for a more loving, doting father than he, so I'm sure either a boy or girl will please him."

Mrs. Scranton accepted her tea from Granny's serving tray and speared a couple of pieces of *chami* melon before she settled back in her chair and spoke again.

"When we talked together that day in Loulie's parlor," she said, "you spoke of the pain you suffer because of Henry's long absences during his journeys into the country..."

"Yes," I broke in, "and you said women married to men like my husband must share them with their calling, their commitments." She nodded, but didn't speak.

"Your saying that helped me," I went on, "because I know it's true and it helps me understand why Henry is so driven by work for his students, for the church, for the whole country of Korea...but knowing and understanding sometimes is not enough. Do you know what I mean?"

"I think maybe I do, but why don't you try to explain it to me, and then we'll be sure."

"You said at the end of our conversation that day that you'd pray that the Lord would help me bear the pain of sharing the man I love with his life's calling. Do you remember?"

"Yes, I think so."

"I appreciate your prayers because I do want to be able to bear that pain, and you're right, of course, that it is painful to share him with another...another love, which is what it is, isn't it? Henry is not exclusively mine. And let me say, Mrs. Scranton, that I'm becoming more personally acquainted with God. I'm learning that He loves me and...and I think I even love Him!"

Again, I shocked myself by the words that poured from my mouth. How could I say such things to another person? Women of our time, and especially those of us with a religious calling, were taught to keep personal feelings buried inside. Nevertheless, I plunged on.

"But back to the problem between Henry and me. Is bearing, only bearing, all there is? I keep thinking we could do it differently somehow...find a way to understand and agree, and work together. Then instead of struggling and competing for the time and attention of the other one, can we ever find common ground for agreement on what matters...and having agreed, pull together?"

Mrs. Scranton sipped her tea and stared into the air in front of her as I scrabbled around in my chair for a handkerchief, then mopped up my streaming tears. "It seems," I said, "that whenever we move beyond weather in our conversations, I end up weeping."

"Yes," she smiled. "I do appear to have that effect on you."

"But it's important in spite of my tears. You help me deal with problems I can't discuss with anyone else."

"Then let's get back to your questions," she said. "Can a missionary's wife expect more from life than learning how to live peaceably with a man consumed by his commitment to evangelize in far-off, exotic places?

"Coupled with that," I added, "is to wonder if she—I—can find an outlet for my skills that will contribute to our purpose in being here, something that is mine to do that makes me a kind of partner instead of a forlorn individual waiting in the rain for a train that seldom comes."

"My, that sounds so sad," she said. "Is that truly the way you feel?"

"Well, a little, at times."

"What about that?" She waved toward the account books spread on the table. "Isn't that a contribution toward building the Kingdom of God? Your Henry has seen some remarkable conversions among the school boys and is convinced future Christian leaders are in the making right now."

"Yes, perhaps it is, in a sense."

"Do you dislike your bookkeeping assignment?"

"Dislike it?" I pondered her question. "It isn't hard for me, I will say that. Numbers and accounts come easily, which is why Henry asked me to do it. He gets things into a hopeless muddle and I'd rather do it myself than have to untangle them when he tries. But as for disliking it, I guess not really, although until recently I didn't see any great value in my doing it."

"Value," she said. "Do you ever wonder how God looks at how we fill our days? Might His sense of value ever differ from ours?"

And with that strange question hanging in the air between us, Mrs. Scranton jumped to her feet. "I teach a class in ten minutes," she said. Then she strode across the room and took my hand in both of hers.

"May I pray with you before I go?"

Her request set me back a bit, for no one had suggested such a thing to me ever before. Oh, Mother heard my prayers at bedtime, and Henry and I, and Alice, had family worship each evening he was home. But this was different.

No answer was required of me, however, because my formidable friend closed her eyes and addressed the Almighty in warm, intimate tones as if she were talking to a familiar friend. She asked that Friend to open my eyes and comfort my heart. "We must talk again," she said after her final amen. I nodded, mute, as she bustled off to class.

Chapter 17

Depending on God

Shortly after my most recent encounter with Mrs. Scranton I began feeling some better. Humidity dropped and life grew more tolerable. Hope blossomed. Maybe things would settle into normalcy, whatever that might be. But then one night while we three slept safely in our beds, we thought, a thief took a key from Henry's pants pocket, opened the safe and stole $160 in silver.

A wild rain storm had come up and we'd dashed around the house closing windows and doors against its lashings. The storm had broken the heat and as soon as we had secured the house, we fell into a deep, relaxed sleep and didn't hear the thief prowling about our rooms.

When we discovered next morning what had been done to us, we felt exposed and vulnerable. Unsafe and unprotected. At first I blamed the whole miserable occurrence on our being in a foreign land away from the securities of our homeland, a typical reaction for me at that point. But then I surprised myself with a different point of view. It happened while Henry and I discussed the theft. He was upset, to say the least.

"One of the servants...it had to be. No question about it," he ranted. "He rifled my pockets in the middle of the storm and used my keys to open the safe!"

"It's awful, frightening, really, not to feel safe in one's own house, isn't it?" I said with a shiver. "At home in America we could call in the police and feel relatively confident that something would be done about such a crime."

"Oh, I can report this to the authorities and I will, make no mistake. I've no doubt they'll take action, harsh action. It just bothers me, though, to the bottom of my soul to be stolen from. Why, in New York when I went to be interviewed for missionary service, some thief picked my pocket on the street. He relieved me of my wallet, my train ticket and my money, what there was of it."

"Did the police catch him?"

"No, they said it was impossible and that I should be more careful in the city. I felt like they'd seen this happen so many times to country boys like me that it was all they could do to keep from yawning in my face."

As I sat and rocked for a moment, thinking over what Henry had just told me, my anger and frustration at being a victim in this Oriental country began to dissolve and drizzle away. Thieves are thieves, whether in Korea or the United States. My premise that we were victimized by being missionaries in a strange land hadn't a leg to stand on. Didn't Henry just say that he'd been robbed in the U.S., a victim on home soil? Life has its problems and wicked people will mistreat you no matter where you live or what your calling is.

"...and I shall write and tell them what I think, don't you agree?"

"What, dear? Sorry. My mind wandered for a moment."

"I was saying, Ella, that the $160 was lost through no fault of mine. After all, Scranton dragged that old safe over here in his baggage and I fell heir to it when I was appointed treasurer. I intend to write mission headquarters and request them to stand the loss."

He didn't wait for a response from me. He needed none, really, for his mind was made up and off he strode to write his letter.

"This baby will surely be born soon," I grumbled to myself a month later. "And surely I will feel better when he is." Weight and weariness immobilized me and I was miserable beyond measure.

Henry Dodge Appenzeller came to our home November 6th. He was a good baby, but jealous Alice clamored for attention every waking minute. She obviously felt displaced as the center of the household. I thanked God Henry was there to help. But that didn't last long. His being there, I mean. Soon he was off "for just a few days, Ella, I promise," to the south. We missionaries, our various groups, were trying to agree on where to place other mission stations when the political situation eased, so Henry and Horace went to spy out the land just like Caleb and Joshua. Their plans did not take me by surprise that time and I managed to smile at my husband when he was dressed, loaded and ready to go.

Mrs. Scranton had stopped by earlier "to consult about a Christmas party for my girls," she said, and we did make some plans, it's true. She examined my face carefully for signs of problem, I presume, over Henry's going. Funny, though, I didn't mind. I finally learned to be glad she cared enough to take time to inspect my face, to check on me. When she stood to go, she said, "Shall we pray together, Ella, before I go?"

I nodded yes as she seized my hand and began addressing the Almighty. I still felt a touch awkward when she did this, but on balance I sensed that it helped. My spirit stabilized and I felt better able to cope.

The holidays passed with a whoosh that year, a tendency that accelerated the longer we lived in Korea. Loulie had Christmas dinner for the missionary community at her house. By then, 1889, Seoul hosted too many Westerners for us to all dine together; borrowed chairs and tablecloths could stretch only so far. Embassy and business people made their own plans. I wondered if they weren't more pleased to be able to enjoy spirits with their holiday dinner, something they couldn't do with us straight-laced missionaries.

It felt odd to have Dr. and Mrs. Allen back in Seoul after their home leave but not to see them at the missionaries' Christmas dinner. His problems with his mission co-workers never resolved and I heard he was applying for the secretarial position at the American Legation. While still friendly with Henry and me (not so with many of the others), he removed himself from fellowship with missionaries and set himself up as leader and arbiter of other segments of the expatriate community there.

On Sunday nights Mrs. Scranton led special worship services for Korean women, who, she said, felt more at ease attending without men. "This fits in better with the Korean way of doing things," she claimed—and was right as usual.

"...and Ella, I would like you to come when you can. More women are attending and perhaps you could assist me."

"Oh, I'm not sure my language is good enough to do something like that," I protested.

"Well, there's no better way to improve your Korean than to listen to it and to use it," she snipped.

"What do you want me to do?"

She took a deep breath, then bit her tongue and looked at me a long moment. "Why don't you just come and sit in on the service for the time being?" she said finally. "Let's don't worry about you *doing* anything just now. Can your servant watch the children for an hour?"

"Yes, I think so. Yes, all right. I can do that."

Mrs. Scranton swished away, headed for her next duty like a steamship making for the open sea. As I bobbed in her wake, I surprised myself by enjoying the movement and wondering where her momentum would take me.

———————————

A heavy sense of foreboding hung over both Henry and me one morning early in March, which was odd because we knew mail would come that day. Usually mail day lifted our hearts and set us humming through our tasks, but not this time.

A student detained Henry just as he was about to walk around to the legation, so I went. Among our packet of letters was one from Byron that broke my heart. Father is dead. My own dear father, sick, dead, and buried, and I am on the other side of the world, a bitter, awful thing to have to bear.

I couldn't even weep for days. My loss lay like a block of ice somewhere between my heart and my lungs. Henry hurt, too, and

Alice peered into our faces trying to fathom what has gone wrong in her world. Her Papa explained that Grandfather Dodge had gone to heaven, but her only knowledge of Grandfather Dodge was a lovely Christmas letter he wrote to her. Little Henry sensed nothing amiss. How it pained me that neither of our children would ever know their grandfather.

Word of my father's death spread through our community and friend after friend came to call, to express sympathy and love, to offer help with the children, to leave a bit of food. Koreans from PaiJai and the church congregation as well came to sit with us for a few moments and to share in our sorrow. Instead of talking, they sat quietly in the parlor and prayed, gently rocking their bodies back and forth and murmuring, "Chu-yo, Chu-yo, Oh, Lord! Oh, Lord!"

All of this comforted me. I began to know I was not alone. I soaked up love and concern from my neighbors and friends who said to me time and time again, "How wonderful to know that your father is in heaven and that you will see him again someday."

Such comments are common amongst Christians and could be thought trite and empty, but not to me, not then. And being confronted by the death of someone close, someone I loved so much, the assurance of heaven and of reunion someday eased my aching, icy heart. I felt loved and comforted not only by my friends, neighbors and co-workers, but by God as well.

Henry prepared a brief memorial service, more of a eulogy and prayer, I guess, for the following Sunday at Union Church. I brought some forsythia into the house to force into bloom. These hopeful yellow blossoms I took to the service.

———■———

Mrs. Scranton turned out to be not invincible after all. The flu marched through our ranks, sending most of us to bed for a time. It sapped energy from the stricken ones for weeks. Even Henry missed several days of school until the pressure of not knowing what was going on drove him from his bed and back up the hill to his classes.

Mrs. Scranton tried similar action after a few days of her illness but collapsed on the floor in front of her girls. Her son, Will, came over to talk with Henry and they concurred that he should take her to Japan to recover. We tended to forget, given her hard driving ways, that she was older and more susceptible to debilitating illness than us younger ones. I've always felt sorry I wasn't more sensitive to her needs. I'd been too caught up in my own bereavement, I guess, to notice someone else's problems.

Miss Rothweiler, one of the single women who had joined our group, and I fell heir to the women's service on Sunday evenings due to Mrs. Scranton's sojourn in Japan. Before the onset of this crisis I found I could follow quite well what was said. But when I was required to lead the service it wasn't so much a case of speaking Korean as it was of speaking at all. My hands turned to ice and my tongue grew thick and stiff.

We lined up Henry, Brother Ohlinger and others to do the preaching but we were still responsible for everything else. Miss Rothweiler was more experienced by far than I, and I wondered at times if she wasn't impatient at my tentativeness and fear. She kept herself pretty much in check, however. Maybe she could see how hard I was trying.

Meanwhile little Henry grew more cunning every day. I felt convinced he would be as handsome as his father; he already had the same squared-off chin and heart-melting smile. The servants vied for the opportunity to trot him around on their backs, for this is the way Koreans transport their children. He loved it.

Alice insisted that Granny tie her rag doll to her back in the same fashion that Korean mothers carry their children. When she played house, her "house" was far more Korean than American and she chattered away with the helpers in perfect Korean. When she talked with Henry and me she sprinkled Korean words in among the English when they suited her meaning more precisely. She didn't know she was juggling two languages; she was just talking, that's all.

Five years had passed since we came to Korea; young, untried, eager—well, Henry was eager. We plunged in to our new assignment determined to do our best to introduce Christianity in this heathen place. "Heathen" was how we thought of Korea and Koreans at the time and in such thinking it was as if a gulf, a chasm, yawned between us. How different, how wrong-headed we thought them to be. I expected never to feel comfortable there.

But five years later? I sensed the chasm narrowing as I felt more at home, more familiar with this intriguing, at times repugnant, land and her lively, witty, strong, naive people.

Henry and I had to learn to live with each other in marriage even as we learned to live and work in a foreign land. Often we found it difficult to keep our purposes clear both in our missionary ministry and in our marriage. On the plus side, we had two beautiful children, a comfortable house (although people at home would find it odd in places), a congenial community of friends and co-workers, and plenty of meaningful work to do.

Matters either unresolved or requiring further attention included ministry opportunities for Henry and for me, occasional threats to our health, and the resolution of my problem with his absences. I truly felt as if I would overcome this last one in time, although I wasn't sure when the final solution would appear. We Christians talk long and loud about the faithfulness of God, I mused, so I shall depend on Him to provide the answers. I would appreciate a little more speed on His part but even so, I'll wait.

I had no other choice.

Chapter 18

Dealing With Realities

That next summer we took the same house on the bluffs overlooking the Han River near Mapo. This time, however, we Appenzellers rented the entire house for our growing family rather than share it with others. Horace and Lillias rented another nearby, which made our holiday just about perfect.

That July we celebrated our special American holiday by packing a huge picnic lunch, dressing in our coolest clothes and renting a large boat complete with a man and a boy to scull us about. It was wonderful. We sang, ate and laughed like fools. Alice went in swimming with her father and Horace joined them. Lillie and I stripped off our stockings, hoisted our skirts and shamelessly paddled our feet in the cool water off the stern of the boat. The two boatmen squatted on the bow and discreetly stared off at the horizon. Such a display of foreign female skin must have stretched their tolerance level to the breaking point. I know they had plenty to tell their friends that night about the bizarre behavior of the big-nosed foreigners.

The Underwoods stopped in for a late cold supper with us; all we did was eat up leftover chicken and potato salad from our voyage. I found a tiny U.S. flag in Henry's drawer and stuck it up in the bowl of salad. Little Henry kept reaching for it from his Papa's lap.

"Here, let me hold the little tyke," boomed Horace. He pushed his chair back from the table and made a lap for our baby son.

"Isn't he wonderful?" he said to Lillias. She nodded and smiled at her husband, then cut her eyes in my direction for a moment. We both knew that Horace yearned for children.

"Nothing like babies to create a family circle," Henry said, eager to help his friend further his cause. Just then Alice shrieked, a split second before we heard a dreadful crash in the bedroom. I jumped up and dashed in to see what happened, Henry hard on my heels.

There stood Alice on a chair before the chest of drawers. The large mirror belonging to the chest lay in shards and shivers on the floor.

"Papa?" she squeaked. "Mama, I didn't mean to. I'm sorry! I just wanted to see if I looked nice."

"Are you all right? Are you cut? Do you hurt anywhere?" We patted and poked Alice all over, trying to discover if all the damage had been limited to the mirror or if she were injured at all.

"If you looked nice?" Henry gave her a bit of a shake in disbelief.

"Ye-e-es," Alice said, aware that she was on shaky ground and probably headed for punishment. Then I noticed something I had missed to that point, given all the noise and excitement.

"My crystals!" Hanging round her little white neck and down over the front of her dirty pinafore were the Austrian crystal beads given me by my parents when I graduated from high school.

"They didn't break, Mamma! I just wanted to see how pretty they are in the mirror."

"Yes, all well and good," said Henry, "but while you're trying to admire your appearance you could've killed yourself...and you did destroy the mirror...and in a rented house to boot."

"What's a rented house?"

"Don't be impertinent!"

"What's pert—" Sensing she hovered in dangerous territory, Alice stifled her ceaseless questions for once and rather than clambering down off the chair on her own, which she was perfectly capable of doing, she raised her arms to her Papa and gave him a tiny beseeching smile, convincing him that he was the only man equal to the task of helping her down to the floor.

I stuck my head into the kitchen and asked Granny to sweep up the broken glass in the bedroom. All three of us returned to the dining table and the patient Underwoods. Horace handed over little Henry to me with some relief, it seemed, and we explained to them what had happened.

"Ah, yes," said Horace, "what was it you were saying, old friend, about the wonders of having children?"

Henry grinned, and then changed the conversation to plans for their next country trip, come fall.

———————◼———————

Mid-September I finally found the courage to invite the Allens over for dinner. We roasted a chicken, which turned out to be surprisingly tender, balancing off the biscuits that baked too brown on the bottom. A piece of melon and some ginger cookies eased our thoughts away from the meal's earlier shortcomings.

All through the meal Dr. Allen talked non-stop about the misadventures of medical work here in Seoul and I don't think he knew what he was eating. Such a fuss between him and John Heron.

"Jealousy, that's all it was," he trumpeted.

Henry's mouth was full of crunchy biscuit at the moment so I asked a question: "Jealousy of whom?"

"Heron cannot stand the idea that I got here first and enjoy such a cordial relationship with the royal family. Added to that, the home office stated clearly that he was to assist me in the hospital, an assignment with which he struggled from the beginning. From somewhere he gained the notion that he should be equal to me in authority and opportunity, an idea that was pure nonsense to anyone who has half an eye to see with."

On and on he went, oblivious to our reaction to his self-serving proclamation of the difficulties that had threatened to bring down their efforts in Korea. His wife sat silent through it all, daintily picking at her food. When I asked my question she raised her eyes to mine for a long moment and I wondered if she were asking me a question of her own.

"Do you dare?" I felt her inquire, and I realized that here was a woman, old long before her time, who was completely submerged—obliterated, really—by the force and twists in personality of the man she married. She was in her middle thirties at the time but she seemed ancient already.

As I listened to Dr. Allen's monologue, broken infrequently by a judicious comment or question from my husband, the realization washed over me that we all were so young, we who came knocking on Korea's doors to begin Christian work there. Our nearest seniors in experience and authority were days away in Japan. All of us who went there first were on the sunny side of thirty, straight from training of some sort or other with no experience whatsoever behind us.

Small wonder that Allen and Heron found themselves deadlocked in just how to go about things, but how sad that their struggle caused all their co-workers to take sides and nearly to sink their ship. I know Horace Underwood and several of the others came within a whisker of quitting Korea.

We on our side of the compound wall were not entirely pure either, for we had our set-tos over petty things. We watched to see if one was working harder than the other, if he is enjoying more success than I, if that family brought to Korea more comforts and luxuries than ours.

I am sure this is why Loulie became so upset when she visited our home that first time. It took me by surprise because I'd never experienced anything like this before. But lest I come off as the fair haired innocent, I admit to enormous jealousy and animosity when Will Scranton reported in prayer meeting about the growing number of converts to Christianity as a result of his medical practice.

"Why should this be so?" I had raged inside my head. "Henry works hard, too, but he's stuck in education and cannot do the thing he loves the most. If only he could preach freely and evangelize, you'd soon see who had the biggest report to make!" In those unnatural circumstances we regularly fell into such petty squabbles, which must have made God sad.

I found it interesting how calm Henry remained throughout that evening as he listened to Dr. Allen. He walked a careful line, never taking sides outwardly. He did not antagonize our dinner guests nor did he betray the confidences of his friend, Horace Underwood. My husband so often spouted off about volatile issues; I'd never seen this side of his character. We sat out on the edge of our little porch after the Allens left and I asked him about it.

"How did you manage to stay so calm and quiet as Dr. Allen informed us that his is the only expert presence in Korea?"

Henry grinned as he leaned against the post, relaxed and so handsome. "Surprised myself, too," he said. "But I've sensed for some time that there is something sad, something missing in the man."

"Something disgusting about him, I'd say."

"He is terribly irritating, I'll grant you, but he's also a little bit sad. He needs attention and adulation. He needs to be a big shot. It makes me wonder if he was a lonely little boy or if some other misfortune created such a terrible hunger in him."

"If that's the case, he destroys the possibility of receiving that which he craves the most, doesn't he?" I said. "Who can admire or compliment people who are already telling you how wonderful they are?"

"That's the whole problem, isn't it?" Henry chuckled. "We have difficulties among our own group, but at least we don't have Horace Allen to contend with."

"Maybe not, but we do have Henry Appenzeller."

Caught by surprise, he whipped his head around to look at me, unsure of my meaning. Then when he saw me smile he wrapped me in his arms and laid me back on the wooden porch.

"Yes, you do, and don't you ever forget it. I shall show you what contending with Henry Appenzeller really means."

Fortunately no moon lit up the mission compound that night and the gateman dozed in his little shelter. Harry's sudden ardor kindled my own and I acquired a second reason to love that little porch—first, because there we learned to talk honestly with each other and then because we discovered that love is not limited to the bedroom.

Chapter 19

"Floods on Dry Ground"

Henry went traveling again, to the northeast this time and with a Korean believer interested in ministry. Despite all my past troubles, Alice, little Henry and I survived. Even though Mrs. Scranton was away I found myself praying throughout the day, and my heart was comforted. I learned that prayer is not limited to kneeling and to church. I talked to God inside my head no matter what else I was doing and felt sure He heard me.

Henry came home late in November full of stories from the Korean hinterlands. I listened as he spun his yarns and part of me envied the experiences, the adventures, the sights he saw.

Thanksgiving came and went as well, our fifth in Korea. About 20 people, missionaries and children, squeezed round our stretched-out table. Then before I knew it, holidays were behind us. Henry's translation work was perhaps his greatest joy even though it demanded huge chunks of his time and energy. How relieved he was to have more help with PaiJai school, both missionary and Korean. The Scrantons all went home to America because of illness. I missed Loulie, of course, but I also missed Mrs. Scranton, a condition I never expected to admit to. She affected my view of myself and of God more than anyone in my life.

Henry immersed himself in translation work every free minute during the spring of 1891. His preoccupation with it was almost complete. One rainy April day little Henry was sitting on his lap while he and Horace Underwood wrangled over some biblical idiom and how best to say it in Korean. The baby grabbed the corner of a paper lying within his reach, crumpled it quick as a wink and began stuffing it into his drooling pink mouth, cooing all the while.

"No! No, Henry!" roared his father, and when he swept his arm across the table he knocked over the inkwell and drenched their morning's work, that which had not already found its way into our son's mouth.

"Ella!" he bellowed. "Come at once and get this child!" His roar dissolved into a whimper, partly because I plucked little Henry out of his grasp before he finished his command and partly because his weary spirit nearly broke over the ruin of their work.

"Ah, Undie," he sighed, "will we ever finish? I apologize for this disaster."

"Never mind, Appie. I think we can make out what was here. Let's try to re-copy what we can, and if our heads aren't too thick, perhaps we can remember the rest."

I handed little Henry to the servants in the kitchen and helped the two men sop up the mess, which was considerable. When I left the room their two tousled heads were bending over the task of deciphering and re-copying the spoiled sheets of translation.

I stood in the doorway and watched for a moment. How I wished Henry's mother could see him so absorbed in such important work. She would've been so proud. In a recent letter from her she'd recited yet again her nightmare fears that drowning death will steal her son from us all. I felt sorry that she must deal with such gruesome thoughts, but how I wished she'd kept them to herself.

In June we had another "episcopal visit," Henry called it, this time from Bishop Goodsal and his sickly wife. Among other things he preached for our Sunday night ladies. Henry translated. We were feeling the absence of Mrs. Scranton so it was nice to turn the honors over to the bishop.

I was pregnant again and, as usual, not feeling well. Even though the Scrantons were gone, other medical people joined our community and I knew I would be well cared for.

Ida Hannah Appenzeller arrived October 5th. Ida flourished, thank goodness. My ability to nurse my babies never abated, even with this third one. Little Henry was not afflicted with jealousy at being supplanted as was Alice before him. He was cheerful, robust and perfectly at ease in his environment.

I wish I could say the same for his father.

Dear Henry was bone tired almost to the point of exhaustion. He seemed to feel as if the conversion to Christianity of an entire nation depended on him. He was so thin and, worst of all, pessimistic. He stormed back from the school one day in a terrible funk.

"Rank and rice," he fumed. "Rice and rank. That's all they care about. It is pathetic. I just don't understand."

"Henry, Henry. What is it? Sit down," I pushed him into the rocking chair, "and tell me what has gotten into you."

"Bring tea," I barked to the cook, then I shifted Ida to the other side and settled down to hear what had got the poor man in such a state.

"Oh, it's nothing new," he groaned, rubbing a hand over his frowning face. "I'm just so tired of the Koreans basing everything they will or won't do on whether they'll be paid for it or if it means a notch up in rank or status. I'm sick of these people, Ella. Sick of their laziness, their selfishness. They are sneaky and mean. I've spent years learning to speak their language yet they can still mumble or use slang and leave me in the dark and I don't know what's going on."

Then to my utter shock and dismay, he burst into tears. Great sobs shook his bony shoulders and he bent double until his head rested on his knees. I swiftly laid our satiated baby in her little bed, not pausing to burp her this once. Clearly we had a crisis on our hands.

"Henry. Dear, dear Henry." I knelt beside my weeping husband and wrapped my arms around him. Tears rained down my face, too, and wet his hair.

"Ella, I'm sorry. I am so ashamed. Nothing in my life has unmanned me like this. Not family death, nothing. I just can't go on. It's too much. Next June we go on furlough. Shall we stay home? Aren't seven years enough?"

"You mean resign from the mission and not return to Korea?"

"Yes, that's exactly what I mean. I could pastor somewhere, or each. Anything would be better than squandering my days among people who aggravate me beyond belief. I want out, Ella. I want to be in America where I can understand what's going on, where people think and act as I do, where it's home."

For once I had nothing to say. How many times I had toyed with thoughts of abandoning our missionary obligations and taking up a normal life at home. But Henry? Never.

Henry rose from the rocker, ran both hands back through his hair and then blew his nose with a great honk. "I'm going to walk out to South Gate," he said without looking at me. "If you don't mind, I'd rather go alone."

―――――――✦―――――――

Shortly afterward scarlet fever swept through Seoul and we did not escape this time as we did during the cholera epidemic. Both Alice and little Henry took ill. Baby Ida was spared. My memory of those days of their illness is a blur of tears and prayer and round-the-clock care.

Horace Allen, although by then he headed the U.S. Legation and did not practice medicine, insisted on assuming the care of our family. I know his advice and ministrations kept Henry, Ida and me from taking the fever along with Alice and little Henry. We owed him a great deal. But even more dramatic than our survival of scarlet fever was what happened one Sunday in January.

Right after New Year's Henry was to preach for Seoul Union Church. I wondered how he would manage to do this; for weeks he had been so low emotionally and physically. We had not talked again about leaving Korea since the day he sobbed out his anger and discouragement in our rocking chair, but his old buoyancy never came back.

Little Henry and Alice were still in bed with scarlet fever but Horace Allen said the worst had passed so I decided to attend the service because Henry was preaching. The servants could surely watch the children for an hour and I had already made arrangements for some of the other women to handle the evening Korean ladie. service.

Henry went early to the meeting hall as he always did when h bore responsibility for a service, but I slipped into the back at th last minute. I wondered how he would manage to preach around th leaden heart he'd carried within him for all those weeks.

"Turn with me please, dear friends, to the book of Isaiah, chapte 44, and let us read together verses three and four." Henry's thin fac looked much older as the cruel afternoon sunshine created dar shadows in the lines across his forehead and around his mouth. Hi too-big shirt collar stood out from around his neck like a life preserve around a flag pole.

"'For I will pour water upon him that is thirsty, and floods upo the dry ground: I will pour my spirit upon thy seed, and my blessin upon thine offspring: and they shall spring up as among the grass, a willows by the water courses.'"

I can't remember his sermon outline but I do remember some o what he said because it was as if he was talking to himself and th rest of us were mere eavesdroppers.

"The world needs men who believe something. A negativist ma make much trouble but he never inspires confidence.

"Ten minutes of rain in a drought will do more good than te times the same quantity from a watering pot."

Then he talked about a period in our U.S. history when people' interest in things of the spirit dried up, but during that part my min wandered back over our seven years here in Korea. I thought abou all the hard work we put in just to create a home and to discover wha kind of missionary work would be acceptable here.

Illness, riots, threats and dangers, homesickness and death Misunderstanding and separation between Henry and me. Painfu problems with our co-workers. So many difficulties that sap one' energy all piled on top of work and more work, in Henry's cas especially.

"Oh, that floods may come!" Harry's voice grew stronger, younger and I could see he was pouring out his hunger for renewal an sustenance for his own inner self. "Floods may damage the plasterin and frescoing in some of our fine churches *(Not exactly a problem in Korea at this point, I thought.)* but let them come. Our ecclesiastic robes may be so drenched that we can't wear them any longer, but let the floods come. Some of our darling customs and institutions built upon sand may fall, but let the floods come...."

Then Henry stopped in the middle of his oration and looked at his audience, shoved his sermon manuscript into his Bible and said, "Dear friends, rather than continue this sermon as I planned it, I must tell you a story."

Then simply and honestly, the dear man told our friends and fellow missionaries how weeks ago he had reached a point in his own life where—weary in mind, body and spirit—he found only anger and despair in the reservoirs he'd always assumed were filled with a limitless supply of wisdom, good will and the ability to teach Koreans and introduce them to faith in God.

"I am astounded and ashamed to discover that I lack the will to go on. I dread each morning when I must walk up the hill to the school. I find no love in my heart for the students or for my fellow teachers. In business dealings I am harsh and cross, though God knows some local people can push a man to the wall."

I gasped when Henry said that—was he carrying this honesty business too far?—but was relieved to hear an understanding chuckle ripple through the crowd.

"I see only the dark side of things, the negatives with which we contend in this far-away place. I dislike and resent the characteristics and personalities of the people around me and, God forgive me, I've let them know it more than once. My heart and soul are like parched ground and I speak to you today from a desert place."

I was so glad to be in the back of the room because to hear Henry bare his soul in this way broke my heart and my tears brimmed over.

"As I flipped through the Old Testament seeking an appropriate sermon topic for today, I read these verses in Isaiah about floods of water poured out on dry ground. They appealed to me so I wrote a sermon that lectured you, and all of Christendom for that matter, about how we need floods of zeal and blessing from God.

"But all the while, dear friends, all the while I wrote about what you should be, I knew in the bottom of my soul that thanks to my weariness, discouragement, anger and poverty of spirit, I had decided that when we sail to America this coming summer to begin our furlough I would turn in my resignation to the mission office and never return to Korea again."

Here Henry broke again as he had in the rocking chair at home. A collective gasp went through the crowd, just a small one, and then a silence took over that was so thick I felt I could touch it if only I tried. But I was nailed to my seat. I couldn't move so my tears rained down on my white shirtwaist making little ovals of wetness and salt.

Henry spoke again, choking on his tears, "...and so, dear friends, I share with you my heart in its darkest, driest form and I tell you honestly, I need God to pour living water on me for I am more thirsty than I knew it was possible to be. I yearn for Him to flood the dry ground of my life. Otherwise I can't go on."

Horace Underwood, my husband's dear friend, broke the silence that gripped us all when he rose and raced up to where Henry stood. First Horace gripped Henry's hand, and then he dropped it and wrapped his friend in a big bear hug.

"I too need what you are talking about, Appie," he said, and then tears began their trek down his cheeks. The room filled with the sound of sniffs as Horace and Henry sat down in front together. Then someone began to sing:

> *What a friend we have in Jesus,*
> *All our sins and griefs to bear,*
> *What a privilege to carry*
> *Everything to God in prayer.*
> *O, what peace we often forfeit,*
> *O, what needless pain we bear,*
> *All because we do not carry*
> *Everything to God in prayer.*

As I looked around at the people, most were sitting with eyes closed as they sang the words of that dear old hymn. Maybe they felt as I did, that we were hearing the words for the first time. Maybe they sensed, too, that Jesus is a Friend available to bear our sins and grief, that it doesn't all depend upon us.

Someone else began to sing:
I need thee every hour, most gracious Lord.
No tender voice like thine can peace afford.
I need thee, O, I need thee,
Every hour I need thee.
O, bless me now, my Savior, I come to thee.

Yes, we'd all come, led by Henry's honesty and pain, and as we sat there quietly it was as if the Lord gently touched us each one and from His touch we gained health of spirit, strength of heart, and renewal of will. He poured his blessing on His offspring—that's us—and His floods on our dry ground.

Henry and I walked home hand in hand, not talking. I sneaked a look at his face and I could see that although the lines remained—they always did—the tension was gone, replaced by peace. When we reached our little porch he turned to me and laid the palm of his hand against my cheek.

"I love you, dear Ella," he said. "I value your strength, your humor, your balance. And I think, so long as God stands by us, we can plan on coming back to Korea after furlough. There's still so much to do."

Chapter 20

Home Again—USA and Korea

In early June 1892, we sailed for home! I couldn't believe that furlough time had finally come. For the preceding year my anticipation built to such a pitch that giddiness and joy threatened common sense at times, and I didn't even care. At least I made poor old skinny Henry Appenzeller grin once in a while.

One day we laughed so hard over choosing what to pack in the trunks to ship home that the children stopped their playing to stare warily at us, confused as to why Mama and Papa were carrying on in such a hysterical fashion. Then they caught the hilarity—it spread like measles—and began laughing with us, hopping and dancing and grabbing each other until the servants peered around the kitchen door asking, "What's the matter? What's going on?"

It all began with Henry's raincoat, the one that came out to Korea with us, brand new and very smart-looking—then. The same coat that caught in pools the rain that sloshed in through the ship's portholes when I was bitterly ill. The one with which my husband sheltered me so tenderly as we rowed toward shore when I told him Alice was on the way. It always hung behind the door of our house unless Henry rolled it up and tied it behind the saddle when he rode off on one of those pesky country trips.

"It's been my bed cover more than once," he said. He was defending his decision to take that poor coat back to America with us. "Why, we've spread it out on the ground for a tablecloth, too, and eaten many a meal off it."

"That's evident," I replied.

"I'll need it when I am traveling and speaking in churches. I'm bound to run into bad weather and wish I had a coat. This is a very good one. It was the latest cut and the finest fabric I could afford when I bought it."

"Henry, dear, look."

I flicked his raincoat open and let it settle to the floor. There it lay, stained with tea, soy sauce, grass, and God alone knows what else. Two buttons were missing, one of which must have departed under some sort of stress because it left behind a three-cornered tear that gaped at us like Alice's smile when she lost her first front tooth. I stared at the poor old thing lying on the floor between us and the sight of the grime rimming its collar and sleeves made me want to chuckle.

"Poor old missionary coat," I said, and I touched the tear with the tip of my slipper. "Do you suppose when you show up at churches wearing this that people will more eagerly donate to PaiJai school? They'll see right off that you need help most desperately."

Henry stood tense for a moment, struggling against the grin that tugged at the left corner of his mouth.

"Yes, it might work," he said, succumbing to the silliness, "especially if I wear with it those shoes with the soles worn clear through."

"Oh, most definitely that would enhance the look," I shrieked. "But you must remember to cross your legs when you are sitting on the church platform—how else will people see your hole-y shoes and know how needy you are?"

We were off! Building the most ludicrous images we could think of as to how Henry would present himself to church audiences at home, and the farther we ranged into the ridiculous the harder we laughed. By this time the children were taking turns rolling themselves up in the poor old coat and trying to scare each other.

"And, Ella," my husband said, "if people could only see you when you stumble off the ship in San Francisco after days of seasickness, I am sure they'll agree we are among the front ranks of the Lord's most diligent sufferers."

He guffawed again, and so did I, sort of, but the wind died out o my silly sails about then. I tried not to think about the ship too muc and all those days at sea. At least I wasn't pregnant and had nearl convinced myself that this crossing would be pleasant. How could i be otherwise? We were going home!

Our year in the U.S. was everything we hoped for. We enjoye home and family, good food and American ways. Everyone plied u with mountains of home-cooked delicacies in an effort to put pound back on poor Henry. He joined the effort by eating everything offere to him and looked much better by year's end. Rest and release fron the pressures of Korea contributed to his improvement, I've no doub

Henry traveled and spoke a great deal (with a new raincoat), an enjoyed it enormously. I even did my part at times, telling about th lives of Korean women. We both wore new clothes, properly sobe however, as befits missionaries. How dull.

Best of all, Mary Ella was born April 8, 1893, evidence that dea Henry didn't travel the whole time we were in America. But I than heaven I wasn't pregnant during the voyage home.

By September 1893, we were back in Seoul and the children, fou of them now, kept me more than occupied even with the help of th servants. Granny had to retire, unfortunately. "I'm too old," she tol me, "to care for little foreign children any more. My son needs me a home to watch my grandchildren."

Henry fit himself back into the work, all of it and more than he lef for furlough. He trudged to school in stout new shoes, to translatio committee meetings, to preaching points, and far too soon to th adventures of rural Korea. Little had changed there while we wer gone, according to his reports, and at times I felt as if we never lef at all.

Which wasn't all bad, especially when I think about ou relationships with the people—Korean and foreign—with whom w worked and lived. A quality of intimacy and understanding existe among us that was unmatched by anything I felt during our year a home, except for dearest family members. And even with family it was different. We spent huge blocks of time explaining our life and work in Korea to them, usually stimulated by a random question or comment someone made, but I was not always sure they understood what we told them nor, sad to say, did they seem to find our replies all that interesting.

But back in Seoul Henry and Horace could shout at each other across the dining room table about Korean verbs with complete safety and understanding. Loulie and I once again could gossip about our neighbors and brag about our children over tea, while Mrs. Scranton kept our minds on things that really mattered, like prayer and building the Kingdom of God.

Henry and George Jones, our new colleague who lived and worked in Korea's port city, wrote and telegraphed back and forth between Seoul and Chemulpo doing mission business and complimenting each other from the depths of friendly, manly love and mutual regard. And I savored the warmth and joy of the welcome of the ladies of the Sunday night worship service.

"Oh, you've been gone so long," many of them said.

"Did you rest well back home in your native place?"

"Have the children grown?"

"Have you forgotten all your Korean?"

"Please come back and work again on our behalf."

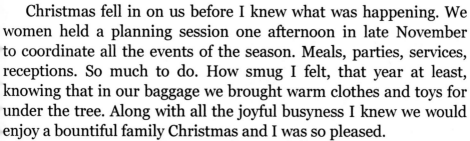

Christmas fell in on us before I knew what was happening. We women held a planning session one afternoon in late November to coordinate all the events of the season. Meals, parties, services, receptions. So much to do. How smug I felt, that year at least, knowing that in our baggage we brought warm clothes and toys for under the tree. Along with all the joyful busyness I knew we would enjoy a bountiful family Christmas and I was so pleased.

That same December Korean politics churned in their usual stir. This time the Tonghaks, a religious sect with political goals, were making trouble about the country. We felt relatively safe within our protected compound as we wondered if hostile action might erupt in the capital. None did and we worked through our days, hoping that matters would settle enough so that we could take a deep breath. But come April a horror broke over my head unlike anything I'd ever experienced before.

Dear God in heaven, that country had to be the most barbaric place on the globe! I still rage over that terrible thing. I had walked out to South Gate late one afternoon with the baby who was feeling left out of the older children's boisterous games. As we approached it I could hear the buzz of a crowd of people, more noise than is normal from the adjoining market. The guards who normally lounged about the gate and greeted us when we came were swallowed up by the crowd, and I wouldn't have been able to see them at all without their tall hats sticking up above the melee.

Because most people were coming in through the gate, returning to the city apparently, I foolishly decided to push against the crowd and go out where Mary Ella and I could enjoy spring among the pine trees. But rather than April's gentle joys, I saw the most disgusting, bizarre display that any human being was ever required to look at.

Mary Ella was a year old by then and quite a load to carry, but I settled her on my hip and pushed against the river of people flowing through the curved-top opening in South Gate. I used to say, "Excuse me, please," when coping with Korean crowds but I learned to do as they do: "Get out of the way, please. Make way!" I shouted, although neither politeness nor demands made any difference.

We squeezed through the gate at last and I expected to break free of the crowd, but it was not so. Even though it had seemed that everyone was pouring back into Seoul from out there, I discovered just as many people milling about outside as there were on the inside. But I could see what had drawn them to South Gate.

Yes, I could see, but I'll never understand it if I live to be 112.

Stabbed into the dirt outside the gate and surrounded by milling, chattering, gesticulating people was a pole, perhaps eight feet tall. And impaled on that pole was the blackened, mutilated head of a Korean man caked with filth and indescribably horrible.

"Oh, dear God!" I screamed. I couldn't help it. The people standing near heard me, and tittered. Humiliation piled in on top of my horror.

"Mama? Mama?" Confused and frightened, Mary Ella tugged at my collar and began to cry.

Again, I plunged into the crowd, pushing with my free hand and not caring who I bumped or what they thought. All I wanted was to dash into the safety of the compound walls. Shoving, stumbling, running, I finally broke free and dashed for home, Mary Ella clutched to my shoulder. Young and still untried by obscenities like that, I wondered what kind of people were they who could do such unspeakable things? I was sick—head, heart, and stomach.

The children were playing on the porch so I plopped the baby down with them and ran into the house before they could read my distress. Henry was home for a change.

"Ella, what is it?" He was reading in the rocking chair but jumped up when he saw me. I told him what I'd seen outside South Gate.

"Oh, my dear, I'm so sorry you saw that." He wrapped his arms around me, trying to gentle my trembling. Then he explained: someone named Kim, a Korean political reformer, had been murdered in Shanghai and his dismembered body parts shipped to various cities in Korea to scare off anyone else with similar revolutionary ideas. Seoul, Korea's capital, displayed Kim's head.

"It's quite likely we're in for some dicey times. Politics again. China is backing the status quo, as is much of the royal family, and Japan is pushing the reformers. Even the emperor and his crowd don't all agree."

"How are foreigners, especially missionaries, viewed in all this? Are we in danger of such a fate?"

"I don't think we need to worry. Of course we obviously represent Western-style reforms, education, all that, but I expect we won't be drawn into the thick of it if we stay quiet and out of sight as much as possible."

At this point the children swept into the house noisily announcing their hunger and their disapproval of one sibling or another, so our conversation ceased. Dirty hands and tangled hair distracted me from the gruesome warning impaled on the pole outside South Gate.

We sat down to thank the Lord for our fried chicken and mashed potatoes. The children ate my share and didn't even notice.

By the middle of May we learned more about poor partitioned Mr. Kim. The government and the royal family, publicly at least, rejoiced at his death. The display of his body parts was to warn the Tonghaks and anyone else with progressive ideas that such would not be tolerated. We foreigners in Seoul remained unmolested but telegrams from Pyengyang told of terrible problems faced by Korean Christians. Prison, beatings, threats of execution. A missionary doctor in that northern city was refused government protection.

Fighting and bloodshed broke out in southern provinces by the end of May, which involved the Tonghaks. One government official, a magistrate, and his entire family were slaughtered. Government militia took a beating and hundreds were killed.

On June 1st Chinese troops landed south of Seoul to help Korean militia put down the Tonghak rebellion. Then hordes of Japanese troops entered Seoul "to balance the Chinese presence," they said. Henry favored the Japanese over Chinese because, he felt, "they are more progressive, more Western in their outlook, and favor Western education styles."

At last the Tonghaks quieted down and the fighting stopped.

In the midst of all this trouble reaching from Pyengyang in the north to the southernmost provinces, Henry doggedly finalized preparations to print at last the four gospels and the book of Acts in Korean. The committee staged some heated discussions as to which Korean word for God should be used, but once they managed to settle that issue, their first efforts at Bible translation appeared in print and ready for distribution.

Chapter 21

Stranger at the Gate

During the summer of 1894, news and rumors churned through
the city regarding hostile action between Chinese and Japanese
with Koreans in the middle. War loomed and we foreigners would
surely be caught in the crossfire, George Jones wrote Henry daily
from Chemulpo where most of the troops were billeted. I kept several
packed suitcases under the bed, just in case, because George thought
families should escape the danger and go to Japan.

Then on July 28 a sea battle erupted off the coast south of
Chemulpo. Facts and information were nonexistent but George,
who heard the firing, reported that the Chinese were on the run, that
the Japanese won. Young Henry listened to all the talk and coaxed
his sisters to play war with him. The girls were not interested. Alice
preferred playing school on the porch, and what she preferred she
usually got.

On into August George kept saying families should leave. I
brought the matter up with Henry repeatedly but all he would say
was, "Let's wait a little."

By mid-September the way the fighting went—Japan overpowering
China—encouraged my husband. He showed me a copy of his report
to New York.

"The Japanese army and navy are marvelously well disciplined
and hating the Chinese for centuries, they are heart and soul in this
fight. China has no army except on paper. Her staying qualities, we
believe, are great but some of us are under the impression that Japan
will knock her out before she gets her second breath. Only good can

come to Korea. She cannot get lower than she now is. The stagnation of China must be blown up. This is what the Japs are doing most successfully."

Although Seoul boiled with intrigue among politicians and palace personnel, the actual fighting bypassed the city. I forgot to mention however, that on July 23rd Japanese troops surrounded the palace and Seoul was really under their control. They guarded palace and city gates so my old friends no longer supervised South Gate. Japanese soldiers replaced them.

It felt odd to know that we lived straddling the path of a war, until that point in my life something that happened only to other people. But there we were in the midst of one and I thought I was calm; at least I tried to be. I checked 50 times a day, however, that the cases still lay beneath the bed, packed full, latched and ready for us to seize and run. Will it be possible, I wondered, when the time comes, for us all to dash to safety? Or will we be shot in our beds or herded off to some dark hole of a prison?

Of course I kept these thoughts to myself. It's funny to recall though, that I had a continuous tic in my left eyelid. Some wayward nerve there twitched and fluttered. No one noticed, however, not even Henry.

Korea signed an alliance with Japan in late August. The fighting moved far to the north then and was between China and Japan. I pulled the cases out from under the bed, unpacked and returned them to the storage shed. Henry was right.

School, both at PaiJai and for our children, began again in spite of China and Japan snarling at each other over the morsel called Korea. Henry enrolled around 100 boys and introduced Christian teaching to them more and more. After our two older children walked through the gate and headed to the Presbyterian compound to begin the new school year, I dropped into the rocking chair and in a rare moment of quiet discovered how very tired I was.

The war prevented us from taking a holiday and so staying in the city kept us at our work. It seemed only natural to plug away at the jobs when they are still there and so are you. Well, nothing for it, I decided, but to keep putting one foot in front of the other (as my grandmother used to say) and expect God to provide whatever we needed, which I figured He would. But I wondered what He thought of it all.

On December 25, 1894: there was peace on earth, at least within our portion of it, at least for the moment. The children were occupied with their Christmas treasures and Henry sat at the table with his new toys: six theology books. My gift? Some lace-edged handkerchiefs.

But that isn't as dreary as it sounds because for our tenth wedding anniversary just before the holidays, my husband presented me with a very long strand of pearls from Japan. He warned me at the time that Christmas would be "conservative." He's such a dear man, I thought. I only wish he weren't so thin. Even though he ate well, at least at home, he ran off the pounds by the awful pace he maintained. I worried that some dreadful illness would fell him for surely he couldn't remain healthy in that condition. I felt for a moment as dismal as Henry's poor mother in all her worrying about him drowning.

I decided to go and play with Ida and her dolls.

All the talk over the holidays among Korean and foreigner alike related to palace reforms. The victorious Japanese threw thousands of men out of military service. I still missed our friends who used to guard South Gate but they never reappeared.

Eunuchs and clowns vanished from the palace along with the king's nine concubines. Henry called them "mutilated, good-for-nothing tramps." The eunuchs, he meant, and I suppose in a sense he was right but I felt sorry for them. They were trained and physically altered for the sole purpose of royal servitude. What else could they do? The clowns and concubines either, for that matter, although I suppose they could ply their trades in less exalted establishments. What a comedown they all must be suffering, I thought. To listen to the talk at the women's worship service, such individuals were looked down upon as harshly as they would be in the West. I ached for them.

Within a few weeks it turned out I must do more than ache, for one snowy January morning I heard a terrible row at the compound gate. I grabbed my shawl and went out on the porch where Cook and some of her friends clustered, laughing and commenting about the fuss at the gate.

"What is it?" I asked.

"Oh, nothing, Honorable Wife. Don't worry. A bad person *(snicker, snicker)* is trying to get in but the gateman is taking care of her."

"A bad person? Her? Who is she? Why is she bad? What does she want?" My questions tumbled out one on top of the other and gave the servants no chance to answer me. As I turned to scuff into my shoes, Cook figured out that I was going to investigate.

"No, no, no! Don't go out! You must have nothing to do with such a person."

"What kind of person?" I tossed over my shoulder as I stepped down off the porch.

"Uh, well, she is...she used to be...she's a very close friend of the king."

As I reached the gate, the guard was pushing at a disheveled young woman dressed in a soiled silk gown. Her elaborate hairdo had not seen its brush in several days and despite her expensive clothes, she was shrieking like one of the market women trying to sell cabbages.

"I must go in and see the foreigners! What kind of a rude, stupid country idiot are you...." And she went on to cast aspersions against the ancestry of the red-faced gateman who grew less gentle each time he blocked the woman from coming in.

I got angry. "Here now, stop it, both of you. Be quiet."

I raised my hand, ready to deliver a few smacks of my own when gateman and visitor alike froze in astonishment at the foreign woman joining their fracas.

"Ai-go, Honorable Wife, have you come?" This common and polite greeting seemed singularly out of place at this moment, but I suppose good manners required the poor man to say it.

"What is the trouble here? Such a racket I've never heard at this gate. What is going on?"

"Oh, Madame, I've come to the foreigners' homes because I have such troubles and problems. I have no place to live and I am hungry, and...."

The gateman tried to do his duty one more time. "Get away from here, you! Don't you know these people are Christian believers and have nothing to do with people like you? Go...."

"Be still, I said!"

He looked at me with mouth ajar. I'd never spoken to him like that before but I was so upset. "Let her pass. I will talk with her."

I beckoned the woman to walk with me to the house and as soon as we turned away from the gate and its defeated guard, I saw the servants still standing on the porch paralyzed with astonishment.

"Make tea," I called to Cook. "We have a guest."

"Tea? Make tea?"

"Of course. Make tea. We are cold and need something hot to drink."

By the time my bedraggled guest and I reached the front door, my anger had all leached away and I began to wonder what I'd done. This young woman, it belatedly occurred to me, was one of the people tossed out of the palace since the Japanese took over, one of the unsavory persons we'd discussed at length just a few days ago.

"Well, nothing for it," says I to myself, "but to see it through."

I stepped out of my shoes and hung my shawl behind the door. The young woman with the tangled hair froze as I closed the door behind her. Was she having second thoughts, too?

"Come and sit here," I said as I pulled out one of the chairs pushed up to the dining table. Not waiting for her to sit, I chose another across the corner from hers and sat down so she could follow my example. She dropped her eyes but moved gracefully to the chair and perched on its edge like a small bright bird on a twig.

Cook shuffled in with the tea pot and two cups (everyday ones) on a tray. Her eyes kept to the floor and two bright red spots on her cheeks told me she was upset. I decided to deal with that later. One thing at a time.

My guest and I sat silent for a moment, sipping our tea and avoiding each other's eyes, according to custom. Then she spoke.

"Ah! This tea is delicious." What she literally said is that it had taste. When Koreans don't like something, it has no taste, so she was complimenting me although we both knew the tea was ordinary, far removed from what was served at the palace.

"Oh, it is nothing special, not worth mentioning," was my required reply.

We waited in silence again for a moment. I heard the floor creak near the kitchen door. Cook was doubtless crouched on the other side, straining her ears to learn what my guest wanted now that she'd wormed her way into the foreigner's house, and to see how much further I would go in flouting propriety and custom. One of the favorite forms of recreation among the compound servants was to compare barbarisms committed by their employers. Well, Cook would have a juicy one to tell this time, I'd already seen to that.

My tousled guest cleared her throat and set her cup on the saucer with a dainty "tink." Keeping her eyes on her hands folded (and trembling) in her lap, she spoke.

"Well, Honorable Wife, it is nothing else but this." (A preamble phrase signaling that here comes the crux of the matter and one would be wise to listen carefully. I listened.)

"For several years I lived at the palace and, um, served the royal family. I received special training for my service although I was but a worthless, ugly girl." (More polite, self-deprecating phrases.)

"But now the Chinese advisers are gone and the Japanese soldiers have come. Many of us who served the king have been thrown out of the palace. We have nothing to eat and nowhere to go, and it is...!" My visitor raised her brimming eyes to my face. Wide and beautiful they were, and full of pain. She sniffed and wiped her tears with the rumpled ribbons that tied shut her *hanbok* bodice.

"Can you not return to your village and your parents?"

"Oh, no! They sold me to the palace. My father would lose much face if I returned. Also, he is a poor farmer and still has young children to feed. I cannot go back!"

"Well...more tea?" I filled her cup, buying a bit of time for each of us.

Then I asked, "Why did you come here? Did you know that foreigners live here?"

"Oh, yes, I knew. I came here once before. The king sent me and several of my sisters to help the foreign doctor, but he sent us back."

"Ah, yes." I recalled the "dancing girls," I believe they were euphemistically referred to, who showed up at Dr. Scranton's clinic in 1886 to "learn Western nursing," so said the explanation, "and serve the doctor in any way he desires." So my guest was one of those.

"I came here because I know that American foreigners are kind and rich. Many Korean people work for you already and I knew that one more small girl would make no difference. I could sleep here..." She gestured toward the space under the dining table, "and I could even work!" Again she raised those incredible eyes to mine, this time sparkling with triumph as if confident that she'd just solved the problem in an obviously satisfactory fashion.

"Yes, well...." Now it was my turn to drop my eyes. What had I gotten myself into by my impulsive charge down to the gate? What would Henry say when he saw whom I'd invited into our home? The memory of the comments at church and among our friends about those deposed from palace service lurked in my head. I could imagine what they all would say if I responded to the pleas of this poor creature sipping tea from my everyday cup.

"How long ago did you leave the palace?" I asked.

"One month ago, Honorable Wife."

"Where have you been since then?"

"Oh, here and there. I had no money so I...then I went to a *kisaeng* house, but..." She glanced at me to see if I knew about *kisaeng* houses and perceived that I did.

"But what?" I pushed her to explain.

"But...the work is hard and many of the girls looked so old."

"Do you dislike hard work?"

"I've never done any. I don't know if I like it or not."

"People here all work hard, foreigners and Koreans alike," I told her. "During your palace service time, did you not work?"

"I sang and played musical instruments. I arranged flowers an did embroidery. These are the skills taught me during my training And I worked very hard to make the king happy, to please him. know how to do this very well. Oh, yes, and I learned to read and t write!"

"How long since you have eaten rice?" I changed the subject.

"Three days," she whispered.

That settled it for the moment. This bedraggled girl with th lovely eyes was hungry, pitifully so. All other issues could be settle later, including my husband's attitude and my reputation in th community. My anger, fueled by sympathetic pain, resumed its burr I jumped up and pushed open the kitchen door, bumping into th eavesdropping Cook behind it.

"Fix some rice for my guest," I commanded. Her mouth droppe ajar yet again. "Do it quickly and also tell the gateman to prepare fire in the servants' bathhouse. She will want to bathe as soon as sh has eaten." I turned to go, ignoring her reluctance, when I thought c something else. "Be sure there is plenty of other food to go with th rice. She will eat it here at our table."

I flounced back into the dining room where my guest sat demurely awaiting her fate. "My name is Mrs. Appenzeller," I told her, knowin the collection of syllables and strange consonants would be difficul for her.

"Yes, Honorable Wife," she replied. "I am Soon Hee."

Chapter 22

Politics: Global, National, Mission

Heavy discussion ensued that night about Soon Hee with Henry, who was upset, to say the least. In an overheated session he accused me of jeopardizing everything he was trying to do by sheltering this immoral, depraved creature.

But at least he didn't throw her out on the street and the girl began by learning from Cook how to wash dishes. Both she and Henry were as stiff and cold to each other as line-hung laundry on a January day. I felt a bit isolated but determined to see it through. I recalled that Jesus spent some time sitting on a Samaritan well curb talking with a woman of ill repute. He acted with courage when his friends threw up their hands in horror, and so, I vowed, would I. Quite a departure, I admit, from the what-will-people-say Ella of not so long ago. Was this what Mrs. Scranton meant by personally relating to God? Was this all His fault?

Fortunate for Soon Hee, I was treasurer of our family and the school. I squeezed our household budget to buy wood to heat Soon Hee's room (thank heaven for the empty storage and servant's quarters that came with our house and which we never got around to converting to other use). I also bought at South Gate Market some warm cloth from which she made herself more suitable clothes. She was clever with needle and thread.

The poor child sensed she was there on borrowed grace so she crept along the walls when she moved from place to place, her beautiful eyes fixed on the floor. I could have shaken Henry Appenzeller for being so stubborn and close-minded.

It took two weeks before Henry and I finally talked like civilized people. Well, it ended in a civilized manner. He had his mind on plans and fundraising for the church he dreamed of building. Part of his reasoning about the need for such a place was the weary business of preaching separate services for men and women. (More than 150 women and girls came to our service on Christmas Day, running ahead by a whisker the men's attendance.)

"What are you saying, dear?" I asked him. "Don't you think it is all right for the women to scrunch up together for their worship time?"

"No, indeed. Before God all human beings are equal and the women deserve dignity and space just as much as the men. I am working on plans that will accommodate both sexes while keeping them separate as Korean custom requires. Look here." He unrolled his sketches to show me the solutions he'd devised.

"Henry, that truly looks wonderful," but as I spoke I laid my hand palm down and fingers spread, on his plans. I looked him square in the eye and said, "Your concern for the women's facilities pleases me deeply and no doubt pleases the Lord as well, for, as you say, He loves all His children equally."

My husband opened his mouth and drew breath to speak but hung onto the conversational high ground and beat him to it.

"It's all well and good, Henry Appenzeller, to work your poor head off to build a church for these people but it's not so good to treat one of them as if she doesn't exist." He sighed and shook his head but kept at it.

"Yes, Soon Hee's a sinner and until now has led a life that nice people like us don't even talk about. But remember two things: first her father sent her into that moral cesspool as an innocent child, and second, she no longer lives that way. She's come to us for shelter and for aid—to us Christians! Are we going to be so self-righteous and so concerned about what someone might say that we will deny Soon Hee the opportunity to meet the Master we've come here to represent?"

I spluttered on some more while Henry stared at me transfixed. His face reddened and I thought he was going to explode back at me in anger. Instead, he bent his head and his shoulders began to shake.

"Henry?"

"Ah, my darling, where did you learn to preach like that?" He raised his face to mine and a wide grin spread from ear to ear. "You even pounded on the table. Shall we take the offering?"

"I don't appreciate you mocking me. This is something I feel very strongly about."

"Yes, I can see that, my dear. And you have converted me, so can we leave off the sermon? I am sorry I've been so narrow-minded and blind, and if the mission calls us home in disgrace, I won't even...."

"Ah! You are a bad, bad man!" I lunged at him but he was too quick for me. He grabbed my wrists and pulled me close by wrapping my arms around behind his back. I struggled half-heartedly although the last thing in the world I wanted to do was escape from the hold the dear man had on me.

"Ella, I'm truly sorry. I shall be as kind as I know how to your little palace stray, and let us both pray that she will find forgiveness for her sins and spiritual direction for her life while she is with us."

———————————◼———————————

One month later word reached Seoul that the Japanese defeated the Chinese navy up north near Manchuria. The war was as good as over and I felt relieved, to say the least. I hoped my twitchy eyelid would give over and we might enjoy some normalcy, whatever that might be.

One March morning I tidied Henry's desk while teaching Soon Hee how to dust furniture. She was wiping the books (seeming to like them even though she didn't read English) and I shuffled together some papers when I caught sight of a letter from William Scranton to Henry. A letter, for goodness sake, when we lived scant yards from each other. Curious, I read it and discovered that trouble lay between them that Henry had not mentioned to me.

William, mission superintendent, was upset with Henry, mission treasurer, for writing to New York with plans and recommendations about building his new church without first consulting with his superintendent. Scranton had written a letter to Henry, next door, rather than talk it out face-to-face. To add to the mix, hospital property was involved and of course, money.

I opened Henry's copybook where he kept replicas of all his letters and found that rather than go to William to solve the problem, he wrote a rather stiff response to the effect that the mission treasurer was not obligated to confer with the mission superintendent on matters of finance or property. It appalled me that Christian friends and co-workers let such mountains rise up between them. Easy enough for me to say as my difficulty with Mrs. Scranton returned to haunt me.

Speaking of Mrs. Scranton, later that spring that formidable and yet dear lady invited Loulie and me over for tea. As I walked across the lawn I wondered if this was to be about Henry's and William's difficulties regarding property for Henry's proposed church, so my heart was thudding hard as I left my shoes at her door. Come to find out, her purposes lay along other lines equally complex. After we'd settled with our tea and gingersnaps, Mrs. Scranton plunged in.

"Ella, your new girl—Soon Hee, is it?—has been coming to my school. Did you know that?"

"No, Mrs. Scranton, I didn't."

I fumbled with what to say next, expecting to be told that Soon Hee's soiled past made her unsuitable to traffic with Mrs. Scranton's Ewha girls. But no.

"Oddly enough, she comes to the Korean language classes. She listens—from the back, of course—while the teacher discourses on grammar and syntax and spelling. Curious, don't you agree? Why do you think she's there?"

I relaxed just a bit and glanced at Loulie. She raised her eyebrows and shrugged. No help there, but I didn't expect any. We had not discussed the Soon Hee business. None of my friends had said a word. Count on Mrs. Scranton to be the first.

"I can't imagine, Mrs. Scranton. I do know she can read and write. Perhaps she wants to improve her skills. I shall speak to Soon Hee, however, and tell her it is not proper for her to intrude on Ewha classes. Please forgive...."

"Nonsense, Ella! The girl is obviously bright and hungry to improve herself, which is why you took her in the first place, I presume." I nodded, astounded as usual at my mentor's turn of mind.

"So let her come, and you might want to furnish her with paper and pens in case she is serious about polishing her literary skills. I shall instruct the teacher to give her a book."

Then the conversation veered off, under Mrs. Scranton's direction, to tea party topics like the cherry blossoms, our children's latest doings and finally the political issues that kept Korea in a perpetual boil.

But my thoughts turned back again and again to Soon Hee's good fortune. The palace castoff, the disgraced woman, would sit and learn with some of Seoul's finest young girls.

———————◼———————

Early that summer I managed to catch some sort of illness that laid me low: dysentery, most likely. I was too weak even to raise my head from the pillow. I wept for no reason at all and every afternoon my body flushed with fever. When Dr. Allen heard of my condition, he walked through the wall that separates us from the American Legation and insisted on seeing me.

He took my hand in his and then said, "Henry, you must take this lady away from Seoul for a rest. Why don't you go over to China, take a house at Cheefoo and let the sea air and change of pace make her well?"

Henry acknowledged the good advice and promised to look into it, but I could tell he was battling in his heart with all the things that tied him there—PaiJai school, translation committee, worship services for the growing number of Korean Christians, fund raising for his dream church. So much to do.

So, we didn't go to Cheefoo. We didn't take a trip away anywhere. And it wasn't all Henry's fault although I knew he would've begrudged the time away. New York refused Henry's request for aid with the expenses. He was upset, of course and vented his spleen in a testy

letter to them so, that done, I knew I could expect him to calm dow
in a day or so.

Then came groundbreaking day for the new church. That shoul
help, I thought. All the funds were not in but Henry went ahea
anyway, of course. I didn't know if the problem between Scranto
and Appenzeller was solved or not. Henry was so pleased that th
Koreans donated so liberally to its construction, so maybe tha
settled matters. Red bricks, steeple, pulpit—just like home it wa:
and the first Protestant Christian church building in Korea. Henr
was so proud.

I was too sick to attend the ceremony.

———————————◼———————————

Unspeakable calamity fell upon Korea in October 1895. W
were dumbstruck and could find no way to explain what happened
Queen Min was murdered! Assassins swept through the palace an
did violence on a whole collection of people, although facts wer
impossible to come by at first. Who lurked behind this crime?

And for us personally, how could such a thing happen just a shor
distance from our front gate? Confusion reigned.

Chapter 23

"Who Is this Jesus?"

Henry went to the Japanese Legation to try and discover from his friend what happened at the palace, what lay behind the queen's death. Soon Hee went into mourning. She asked me for white cloth to make mourning clothes. Still she felt some sort of filial or familial relationship to the royal family.

Shortly after Soon Hee went to her room with the white cloth, Henry returned from the Japanese legation with a long and complex story about a clash between new police (installed since the Japanese victory over the Chinese) and old police (dedicated to tradition and anti-progressive). The latter were favored by Queen Min and her clan, which raised everyone's suspicions, but hard facts are still hard to come by. How did murder of the queen result from a set-to among soldiers? Some say the Japanese were behind the scandal, which made sense.

Little Henry stood around listening whenever topics of murder, soldiers or fighting came up. I suspected he held long conversations with the gateman about it all. In any case, we stood up to our eyebrows in yet another situation guaranteed to keep us foreigners on tenterhooks. The same old question arose: should I pack the cases again?

———◼———

Not long after the queen's death I went to Soon Hee's room to ask her to mend my white shirtwaist, the one I bought in Japan on holiday.

"Soon Hee? Are you here?" I called to her from outside her door.

"Ah, Honorable Wife! Have you come?"

"Yes, I want to ask you something."

"Please come in." She pushed the sliding door back and gestured me into her tiny room as if it were the palace. I sank down on the square pillow with my legs folded under me. Soon Hee, still dressed in white, mourning for her queen, bowed deeply and thanked me for honoring her with a visit. Only then did I unfold my shirtwaist and show her the tiny hole in the right sleeve.

"Do you think you can mend this?"

"This small hole?"

"Yes. I enjoy wearing this so much but it is growing shabby, I'm afraid. You do such fine needle work that I thought you could fix it and no one would know. Of course I will pay you for your work."

Soon Hee nodded, eyes on the offending hole in my sleeve. Then she looked up at me and took a deep breath. "Would you tell me about your God?" she asked.

Startled, I negotiated for time. "What would you like to know?"

"Where is He? What does He do for you? What does He expect you to do for Him? Are you afraid of Him?" The rat-a-tat fire of her questions put my head into a spin but I sensed here was a crossroads moment in Soon Hee's life and in mine as well. I sent up a call for help to the God under discussion.

"Knowing God, our Creator, is almost impossible," I began, "which is why He sent Jesus to show us the way."

"And who is this Jesus?" she asked.

My jaws locked as my brain flooded with a thousand negative thoughts, chief of which was my poor Korean language skills. How many times had I listened to my husband discuss philosophies and religions with his visitors, but only half comprehended the meaning of the words he used. Where were those words now? Why didn't Soon

Hee ask him instead of me? But she hadn't asked Henry; she put the question to me, so I plunged in with palpitating heart and perspiring, shaking hands.

"In our holy book, the Bible, the black one that lies on the table, we are told that God loves the world He made and loves it so much that He sent Jesus, His beloved Son, to make it possible for us to know Him, to relate to Him."

On I went then, trying to explain in the simplest possible terms to this crushed, hurting young woman the mysteries of God's love and His gift of freedom from guilt and fear. As I talked my hands stopped their shaking although my heart still thudded in my chest. My novice status in talking about God meaningfully nearly swamped me but Soon Hee listened in silence, her huge luminous eyes never left my face.

When I finished I looked down and waited, giving the girl time to assimilate what I had tried to tell her and the freedom to react as she chose without fear of embarrassing me. These social gestures meant much in Korea and I was learning to adopt them.

"Well," Soon Hee spoke at last. "Thank you for giving me so much of your valuable time and for sharing these precious words with such an insignificant person. I probably cannot do it well but I shall mend your blouse *(chima, she called it)* quickly and return it to you."

We both stood. Soon Hee pulled open the door, and then swiftly turned my shoes so I could step directly into them as I left her room. Once outside I turned to say goodbye. She bowed low so that I could not read her face. I walked away, beset again with the fear that my language was lacking and my simplistic dealing with Christian theology had left our guest befuddled and probably more committed than ever to her Buddhist upbringing.

After the holidays whirled past us, Henry took to roaming about Korea again, south this time. Soon Hee did not speak of our conversation about Christianity again and neither did I. Doubts and questions troubled me. Was I remiss? Should I more actively try

to evangelize her, push her to accept Jesus as her Lord? Being so
indecisive made me feel inadequate and unworthy as a missionary
but stronger than my insecurities was my inclination to let Soon Hee
decide the timing of our further talks about God. If that is inadequacy
I decided, so be it.

As I pondered those questions, Alice came running into the house
"Soon Hee wants you!" she announced.

The children loved to visit the girl's room, a fact about which
was uneasy at first. After all, her past was hardly one I could wish
to influence them, but neither did I feel comfortable walling her off
from them, so I put God on notice that I expected Him to protect
them from the degradation Soon Hee had endured and left it at that

Alice led me by the hand to Soon Hee's door where she welcomed
me and invited us in. She poured me a cup of barley tea, a humble
drink the people there didn't even call tea; they spoke of it merely
as water, although I found its light flavor and earthy fragrance quite
pleasant.

After tea, Soon Hee reached behind her spreading skirt, brought
out a folded white bundle and pushed it toward me. "I have finished
your mending," she said.

I unfolded my shirtwaist, aware that weeks had gone by since
I left it with her. I'd wondered if she had ruined it and was afraid
to tell me or if mending was too humble a task. But no, Soon Hee
had turned my beloved garment into a work of art. Around the tiny
hole in the sleeve she had embroidered a flower, making the hole
its center. Then she made six other tiny holes and six other dainty
flowers, seven in all on each sleeve. On the cuffs she had worked a
chain of flowers similar to the ones scattered on the sleeves.

"Soon Hee!" I gasped. "How incredibly beautiful this is!"

Alice clapped her hands, bouncing up and down. "Do you like it
Mama? Do you like it?"

"Like it? Of course I do. She's made my shirtwaist into a beautiful
thing like no other. How can I thank you, Soon Hee?"

The lovely young woman bowed slightly with lowered eyes. "If
you like it, even though it is poorly done, I am pleased."

"As soon as the other foreign women see what you have done to his, they are all going to want you to decorate their clothes. I can't wait to wear it and show it off. My husband is sure to admire it, too."

"I am glad it pleases you," she murmured.

I dug some coins out of my skirt pocket and reached across to hand them to her, saying my thanks yet again.

"No, no." She pushed my hand away. "It is a gift, my poor stitches on your *chima*. You gave me shelter and food when I was in such deep trouble. I wish to give you something in return."

My turn to bow my head and acquiesce. I folded the shirtwaist and hugged it to me as Alice and I backed out of Soon Hee's little room, scuffled into our shoes, and returned to the house.

———————◼———————

Spring lingered just outside South Gate and Henry was bouncing about with excitement that had nothing to do with singing birds or blooming forsythia. His feet had not yet touched the floor since he was summoned to an audience with the Korean king. Odd, is it not, that we Americans who fought free from England's royal control should be so awed and thrilled about crowned heads?

The Minister of Education told Henry the king wished to meet him and from then on, nothing was the same. I should say first of all that the poor king, since the queen's death, reigned from under the collective thumb of his cabinet, which in turn answered to Japanese "advisers." His Majesty, shortly after her death, left the palace and scooted off to the Russian Legation, apparently feeling safer there than close to the Japanese who had become in fact the rulers of that poor little country.

Anyway, after consultations with Horace Allen and questions put to Soon Hee on behavior and protocol, Henry marched off to meet His Majesty. His report of the visit ever after caused me to smile every time I thought about it. He required from me much more than a normal amount of priming to give it.

"What happened? What was it like?" I began as soon as Henry returned and seated himself in the rocker.

"Well, we stood around with many others in a drawing room People were coming and going, talking and smoking. Undie wa there."

"Go on," I prompted.

"Then about three o'clock a servant called us. Undie and I followe the Education Minister into an inner room, and there stood the kin and crown prince, right there before us."

Henry sat and rocked for a long moment, rubbing his chin, hi eyes unfocused.

"Then what happened?"

"Um...what? Oh, yes, the king asked Undie how he was."

"What did he say to you?"

My husband looked up at me with a pained expression. "Say? I.. can't remember!"

"Henry Appenzeller! You go to see the king of Korea and you can remember what he says to you! Impossible!"

"Well, it was some sort of greeting, I'm sure. You know how the always do. I do remember he asked the minister, 'Is this the one? th teacher of students?' The minister said yes, I was. Then...and I d remember this part quite clearly...the king spoke favorably of PaiJ and the work we are doing there and said he hoped the time woul come when 1,000 boys studied there instead of 100."

"Anything else?"

"He asked me several questions about our school and the studie the boys take."

"Such as?"

"Ella, I can't remember the specific questions very well. I do kno they were simple ones I could answer with yes or no."

Then he looked at me with the most pitiful expression and sai "I was so nervous that my wits abandoned me completely. My hand trembled so that I clenched them behind my back, and I could nc think of the simplest Korean words nor could I understand anythin His Majesty said to me. I was struck dumb and witless. Can yo believe it?"

I sat on the poor man's lap and cradled his head in my arms. Nc I couldn't quite believe that dear Henry's language skills abandone him at such a moment, but on the other hand, I could. Did not I mumble and fumble when Soon Hee asked me about God? What earthen vessels we are, just as the Bible says. Whatever possessed the Lord to entrust His treasures to us?

Chapter 24

Work Flourishes, Health Wanes

On May 30, 1898, Alice, our precious firstborn, sailed off to Chefoo in China to boarding school, certainly the hardest thing had to face in my whole life—to that point. Street riots and cholera epidemics could not hold a candle to that pain. Our child would eat her meals, study her books, chat with her friends and we'd have no part in it. We'd know nothing about her daily life. When she hurt someone else would comfort her. When she succeeded, someone else would applaud. At least I hoped someone would. Serving God costs dearly, I moaned. But Alice had finished all the levels available in our little English-medium school in Korea, and Henry and I felt sure she needed further education for the years to come. Sending a child off to boarding school was not unknown, especially among those who lived abroad, but the schools were often far away.

Soon after Alice left, dealing with heartbreak of a different sort, Henry wrote to his father begging for financial aid in building the church. He knew, I'm sure, the futility of such an effort; after all, "like father, like son." Henry himself did not part with his monetary assets willingly, and he'd learned such behavior from an expert: his own father. But he couldn't prevent himself from trying. "It is one of the keenest disappointments of my missionary life," he said, "that I have been unable to arouse the practical interest of my immediate family in the work in which I am engaged." By practical interest, he meant of course donations.

And then in mid-June, Loulie and her children sailed for a year's furlough in Switzerland. Will stayed behind to work. I knew I would miss her desperately. My world shriveled. Why do painful events and disasters always come in clumps?

By July I was bedfast with my old stomach ailment. The PaiJai books remained undone. Henry wrote months earlier to our New York office for funds that would enable us to vacation with Alice in Chefoo, but we received sympathy for our plight rather than money for our trip. Given an earlier cut in our salary, we could not afford to go to see our daughter. How I longed for respite from my physical problems. I suspected that, were my heart and mind more at ease, my body would follow suit.

When winter began to clamp down on Seoul, Henry found temporary respite from his woes by being asked to give an address at the dedication of Independence Arch, a newly built monument outside Seoul that sat astride the former tribute route to China. For centuries, Korean government officials mounted small horses or shut themselves into sedan chairs hoisted onto the shoulders of bearers and accompanied loads of desirable goods—a tribute—on a long, overland journey to China. This did not mean that Korea was a Chinese colony; it did mean that in response to the tribute, China allegedly supported and protected Korea. How this all worked out politically is another story, and the height and grandeur of the monument that Henry was to dedicate spoke of the celebration from a Korean point of view—that the tribute was a thing of the past.

Alice came home again in mid-winter from her school in China. She could not take the separation from her family and became ill, so we brought her home just before the holidays.

In February of 1897, the king left the Russian Legation and moved into his palace once more, a different one from the place in which his queen was murdered. He lived then just across the way from us although the high stone walls protected him from our curious eyes. I wondered if he ever peeped over at us.

Finally, months later, we succeeded at something. On October 3, 1897, Henry's feet hardly touched the ground, he was so proud. We worshipped in the new Chungdong church, and he was so thrilled he could not contain himself, lack of family donations notwithstanding. Seeing him so joyful, partly caused by Alice joining church that day bolstered my spirits a little. Will Scranton did the honors for our little girl and he was so moved, he could scarcely get through the ritual.

It was wonderful having Alice at home. Her health improved, but we were hard put to know what to do about her education. She now needed more than was available in Seoul.

Another Christmas came and went without a solution to the problem. The holiday that year was especially festive, however; I remember talking with Henry about it. Because it was too cold to walk out to South Gate, we stayed by the stove and reminisced after the children went to bed.

"Do you remember how homesick we felt our first Christmas here?" he said.

"Oh, yes, I remember. All I could think about was the fact we were not at home with family. I felt so lost and alone."

"And now? How did you feel this Christmas?" he asked.

I thought for a moment. "Why, I don't really know...haven't thought much about it..."

"Exactly! We don't think about it at all anymore. Christmas is a good and happy time for us here. The children tear into their gifts..."

"And when we all get together for Christmas dinner," I interrupted, "we enjoy each other so much. It is festive and warm and...and... merry, isn't it!"

"Do you know," Henry went on, "I missed our Korea friends and co-workers during the holidays when we were with our own families. We hold so much in common with the people here, so much that those at home cannot understand and, let's face it, are not terribly interested in."

He was right, of course. We were different people from the newlywed couple who scrambled across the rocks at Chemulpo still bound by strong ties to home. By 1897, although we would always be Americans and always love our *ko-hyang*, our native place, Korea was home, and the people who knew us best were there.

In 1898, the ever-present problems and difficulties collected in heaps and piles. To name a few:

Henry was very angry with the American Bible Union who billed him repeatedly for a Bible he ordered (my Christmas present) but which he never received.

The pulpit for the Chungdong church, requested from Japan, disappeared. Was it at the bottom of the sea? We never learned its fate.

The Bunkers, who had arrived a year or so after we did, went north to work with a mining company. Henry had come to depend on them at PaiJai, and he was so upset he couldn't even speak of it.

Mrs. Scranton took sick. She and her son, Will, left to join Loulie and the children in Switzerland. I knew I would miss her.

To top off the miserable heap, we learned that Henry's mother died. We'd sent letters to her from Alice and little Henry on the very day the news came to us that she'd gone to heaven weeks before.

But on the plus side of this dismal ledger, Soon Hee still took refuge with us. She filled an important niche in our lives, especially as a result of her various attempts at education, first with Mrs. Scranton's school and then on her own. She developed extraordinary skills with Korean grammar and nuance of meaning, which Henry and Horace frequently called on because Korean thought patterns that shape their speech differ radically from our own. Her insights helped with their vocabulary choices daily. She often perched on a chair at the corner of the table as they grappled with some abstract idea in scripture and she discussed with remarkable authority how best to say it in Korean. Otherwise the two men could have strung a row of Korean words together that made no sense to the one reading it.

She was equally good with the children and I know their Korean language skills were enhanced by the times they played and chatted together. This same girl dusted and swept and helped around the house wherever needed. We'd never talked again about Christian beliefs and I wondered what went on in her mind but didn't feel the time was right to probe.

In November Henry tried to resign as mission treasurer but our co-workers begged him to continue, even when he told them that I was no longer strong enough to keep the books for him. This particular assignment seemed to sap the good health from us both. Henry was frightfully thin and fell asleep in the rocking chair right after dinner almost every evening. My stomach churned at the mere sight of the ledgers and vouchers sitting in a pile waiting for me to post the transactions.

The dear man dreamed of traveling through Europe when we would depart Korea for furlough in 1901. We spent some pleasant evenings pursuing that dream and telling each other all the wonderful sights we would see. Our school days had been filled with pictures and description of places like Rome and Athens, the Swiss Alps and the Danube River. Might we really have the opportunity to see them all with our own eyes?

Late in 1899, little Henry took ill. My work came to a standstill for he liked to have me sit with him. All the other things I normally did were pushed into the background at the request of our ten-year-old son.

We weren't sure what was wrong with him and neither was the doctor. Henry began negotiating with New York about our leaving Korea the following spring in the interest of the health of us all. He wanted me and the children to go to Europe in February or March, put them in school as the Scrantons had done, and then he would come in the summer of 1901.

How did I really feel about Henry's idea that we separate for a year so the children and I could get to a healthier, more restful place? Without question the selfish thought of being away from Seoul in some clean and disease-free Western place enticed me almost beyond reason. I pictured the children frolicking on green grass without stares and comments about their foreignness. I dreamed of green vegetables and fresh fruit, cheese and chocolate.

But then I thought about the Korean ladies I knew and loved from the Sunday evening women's services back before the church was built. Even though they worshipped by then with the men, we remained close and could talk to each other with intimacy and caring. I shall miss them terribly, I admitted, when we finally do go.

And what about my other jobs? The PaiJai books? (Dreadful thought—turned my stomach.) Yes, I hated those books with their precisely drawn lines and marching rows of numbers, some black but more red. But I was the only one to do it, so they pressed in on my brain and I couldn't figure out how to get out from under them.

And Soon Hee? Warm regard built between us and I so longed for her to want to talk again about faith and God's love. She would eventually, I was sure of it, and I wanted to be there when she did.

Henry was concerned about us all (as I was about him), and he wrote to the agent for traveling particulars. Part of me hugged close this fact with joy and anticipation while another part sighed and said, "Oh, no, I can't possibly go."

Then came 1900 and, with it, the possibility of rest and release. The new century didn't feel much different from the old one. By now the children and I held bookings to sail for Europe in April. As he had suggested from the beginning, Henry planned to remain in Korea an additional year and then join us. We expected to stay with Loulie and her family in Switzerland for the summer and then find a school in the fall. He felt sure our health would improve there, and he was working hard to make it so.

But what about his?

———————■———————

Such a fuss erupted over Alice's bicycle just before we left! A fellow missionary family, the Hulburts, wanted to buy it for their Helen, knowing we planned to leave Korea for a couple of years. We agreed and Henry worked out a price, discounting what we paid for it new and splitting the cost of a couple of repairs it needed.

Well, the Hulburts argued about the cost and claimed it was no
in perfect condition. The situation was ridiculous, but it revealed
what short fuses burned in each of us in those difficult times. In the
interests of peace, I felt inclined to accept whatever they wanted to
pay and forget it, but Henry took hold of the issue like a bulldog with
a bone and would not relent.

"They will pay according to the agreement," he huffed, and so the
notes between Hulburt and Appenzeller were frequent and hostile
In a few days they paid at last for the bicycle, but I wondered if we'c
ever have another civil conversation with that family. It was awful
and for once I was not very proud of my husband. He just was no
himself, and I worried.

By May the sun shone again for a time. The New Testament wa:
completely translated into Korean and Henry, Horace and the rest o
the committee were ecstatic. I was so proud! So was Soon Hee for sh
knew she played an important part in its completion. With courtesy
and ceremony Henry gave her a copy, which she received with both
hands and a deep bow.

And then we experienced progress of a different sort. Tha
summer a railroad ran at last between Seoul and Chemulpo. Americar
advisers, brought in by the government, saw to the building of the
line. We vacationed by the sea in Chemulpo and Henry could ride the
train to Seoul, take care of whatever business he must and return by
nightfall. What a joy for him and for us!

The ocean breeze blew cool and good. All of us enjoyed going to
the beach. Thanks to my being away from Seoul's tensions, I even dic
several months' worth of bookkeeping and still felt well. The childrer
looked marvelous and ate like ravenous beasts.

Then, by the end of summer, with little Henry so much improved
we planned to leave Korea—all of us—by the end of September
Henry changed his mind about staying back in Korea, it seemed, anc
with arrangements complete and tickets in hand, all four childrer
could not control their excitement. Soon Hee, however, became quite

solemn. She will miss us, she said, and I believed her. I knew I would miss her as well.

One morning, shortly before we sailed, she said to me, "I am reading God's Book."

"What do you think of it?" I asked her.

"When I read Jesus' words, my heart grows warm. He speaks so often of...of love. Of this love I know nothing."

"This love of which He speaks," I told her, "is the most important part of our faith. He offers it to everyone."

"Yes, I see," Soon Hee replied. "I shall continue to read the Book."

For some reason I couldn't leave it there. I knew we would be gone shortly and I wouldn't see her again for months and months.

"Is there anything else you want to ask me?"

Uncharacteristically, Soon Hee did not drop her eyes but looked straight at me with an expression I shall never forget.

"You say this love is for everyone. Is it for me as well? You know what I was before you led me through your gate."

I took the Book from her hands and turned the pages to the gospel of John and read the story of the woman caught by her neighbors in adultery. We read together about how the people wanted to kill her with stones, as was their custom, and how Jesus said that whoever had never sinned should throw the first stone at her.

When we reached the part where all the woman's accusers had left in shame, none being sinless, and Jesus said, "Neither do I condemn you. Go, and sin no more," Soon Hee's beautiful eyes filled with great shining tears.

"Do you think Jesus's love is for you, Soon Hee?" I asked.

"He loved and forgave the woman in the book, didn't He?"

"Yes, He did."

"Because He loves and forgives women like...like us, then I shall love Him and follow Him all the days of my life."

Soon Hee reached both hands across to me. We gripped each other's fingers for a moment, tears spilling from both pairs of eyes. Then we moved close and slipped our arms about each other, sisters and friends.

Chapter 25

Henry Sails Alone

In October Henry caught up with us at last. I say caught up because of course our departure from Seoul did not go as planned. What ever did?

My husband decided he could not leave the mountain of work still facing him even to accompany us on the long journey home, a journey about which we'd dreamed and planned for more than two years. So even though we knew Henry would stay behind, during the final days our whole family went smiling through elaborate farewell events with the PaiJai boys, the Ewha girls and the expatriate community and then shook hands with dozens of Korean church people at the train station.

The time came. The children and I boarded the Chemulpo train while Henry, with the oddest look on his face, instead of getting on the train with us, braved the stares and questions of our friends as he stood on the platform and waved goodbye to us along with them. Then he turned and went home for a few more days, leaving mouths agape.

When he finally joined us a week later in Japan I asked him, "Did you get it all done?"

"No, I didn't. I did my best but simply could not finish, so I just walked away."

He looked so forlorn and sad that I put my arms around his poor bony body. We stood, silent: worn, tired and relieved to be gone from Korea and our impossible responsibilities. In a few days we boarded a ship in Yokohama and sailed, not toward the U.S. directly but round he earth the other way, a long slow journey to Europe. Sailing from port to port was great fun. We all saw unfamiliar and enticing sights hat set the children (and their father) chattering endlessly.

October 11, 1900—Shanghai, China. This we found to be like a Western city in many ways, with international banks and companies n the tall stone buildings and countless people from all over the world pushing their way through the crowds of Chinese. Henry didn't ike it there. I'm not sure why, because I found it intriguing. Maybe ie needed to recover and rest before he would like anything.

October 16—Hong Kong. Hundreds of bright lights everywhere made me think of a whole collection of Aladdin's lamps lit by a tribe of genies. We saw the Happy Valley race course, foreign and Chinese emeteries, and took tiffin at the Peninsula Hotel among travelers awaiting trains into China. Henry ate everything they offered and I could swear he looked around for more. A good sign, I thought.

October 21—Singapore. The city was busy, interesting and steamy hot. People from a countless variety of countries swarmed the streets, similar to Shanghai and Hong Kong.

October 23—Penang. A crowd of noisy Dutch travelers boarded our ship here.

October 28—Ceylon. Though it was Sunday, the children and I took a carriage and went sightseeing. Henry and Miss Brownlow, a Japan missionary and fellow passenger, went off to find a place of worship. I felt the shift in cultures between here and northeast Asia. The faces and clothing were different, but the crowds were just as dense.

November 3—Aden. "A more dreary spot, barren and cheerless, it would be hard to find." So Henry wrote in his diary; I peeked. It was dry and windy, especially after the green, lush tropics of our last couple of stops.

November 8—Suez Canal. Hot! Henry discussed with the ship's officers the cost to the shipping company to sail through the canal. He liked to know such things. He could not do mission work or school work, and the real, interested, ever-thoughtful Henry was beginning to emerge.

November 9—Port Said. Alice and I bought ostrich feather fan and some fruit from a Greek. I thought, this means we are nearin Europe. Henry got pressed flowers and an olivewood cane from th Holy Land.

November 10—Henry wanted to stay in our cabin while th children and I wandered the ship and took part in the endless time of refreshment offered by the crew. Early that afternoon I went bac for a fresh handkerchief and discovered he'd brought along th treasurer's books from Korea and was trying to catch up. I was wron about him leaving mission work behind.

"I don't think I can do this," he moaned when he saw me standin aghast in the doorway. "My head hurts too much."

I decided to take matters into my own hands. "Put those thing back in the box then," I said, "and don't let's look at them again unt we reach Pennsylvania." With a nod he headed for the trunk roon the wretched books under his arm. I'm confident that my bossines was the right remedy.

November 17—Rome. All the marble made Henry feel cold, bu I could not find words to describe the loveliness, the antiquity. Th children soon tired of huge dark churches and museums, leanin toward their father's view of things. We left the ship in Italy an traveled overland from there by train. The major portion of ou baggage, including the treasurer's books, was shipped on to Nev York.

November 21—Florence. We saw more marble, toured mor churches, and ate delicious food amidst crooked cobblestone streets I could've happily stayed there a while. I bought a beautiful pair c kid gloves.

November 29—Switzerland. We got off the train and into a hotel i Berne. We tucked the children in with books and drawing materials put Alice in charge and then went hunting for Appenzellers. It wa Henry's opinion that this was the region from which his family came We found several and dear Henry enjoyed mulling over family histor with them. Our next stop was Lausanne to meet the Scrantons Loulie and I had much catching up to do. I only hoped we could fine the moments to do so. Our time in Lausanne came and went like dream. Leaving Switzerland was hard since Loulie and I had almost no uninterrupted time to talk. Children and husbands saw to that.

December 10—London. We stayed several days, and visiting historic churches excited Henry. He took the children to see the graves of some of the early Protestant greats. I begged off and enjoyed some solitude in green, cool England. London was decorated for Christmas and a wonderful sight it was. We bought clothing, after which Henry told me money was short and we must be careful. He said we'd be right again as soon as we reached New York.

On January 3, 1901, our long, lovely journey ended, and the Appenzeller family arrived at a rented house in Philadelphia. We found a school for Alice, and Henry filled up his calendar with speaking engagements hither and yon. He was not yet fat by any means but did say he felt less tired and was eating well. The other children went to public school and I spent my days trying to make that house into our home.

By April Alice was down in bed, sick as she could be, but neither the doctor we found nor we could identify the problem. It began with a cold and sore throat she couldn't throw off and then progressed into a high fever. One or the other of us seemed always to be sick with something. I wondered why. Was I doing something wrong in my care of them?

A month passed and the doctor said Alice was run down and bordered on nervous prostration, for goodness sake. He asked if anything might be troubling her and, as we talked about our way of life and her failure to adapt to boarding school, he declared her nervousness came from the prospect of being left alone here in America when we returned to Korea. Before we talked, he feared pneumonia or typhoid fever but after our conversation he was less concerned about those dreadful diseases and more about the effect of our way of life.

Alice remained weak and listless but I thought, hoped, she brightened somewhat. Her brother and sisters romped on her bed and their noise seemed to cheer her. Henry prayed with her and me, and then took off for a ten-day speaking tour. At the end of the ten days, as soon as he came into the house, he was steaming about American ignorance regarding Korea and mission work there.

"I've not met one preacher who can ask a half dozen intelligent and pertinent questions about missions in Korea, even some on the board of managers. They can tell you how Brother Hollow got to Boonetown and why Brother Indifference landed in Collapseville but that's all. We might as well be building a church on the moon."

Instead of getting well, Alice took a case of the flu and frightened us all half to death. Thank God Henry was home. She finally got a little better, and the doctor pronounced her "out of danger."

By June Alice was gaining daily, which encouraged us greatly. What excitement pulsed through our rented house when she dressed the first time in weeks, and we brought her down to the living room. Little Henry, who was patterning himself after his father, insisted that he be the one she leaned on coming down the stairs.

Early that summer of 1901, Henry and I talked about the possibility of his going back to Korea alone. It looked as if I might need to remain in America with the children until Alice grew strong enough, mentally and physically, to go to boarding school on her own. We felt unsure about what was best.

The doctor tilted the balance, however, for he remained convinced that Alice would not be able to enter school for months to come, so with heavy hearts we decided. Henry would return to Korea and the children and I would stay in the U.S. for the time being.

The doctor said to me, "Alice's trouble is nerves. She has malaria more or less, and brought it with her from Korea. Because the emotional trouble fastened itself on her, the malaria had all the chance in the world to flourish."

I didn't know what to say, but that didn't matter because he continued with his bitter information: "If her sore throat had not alarmed you, you probably would have found her dead some morning and never known what was the matter with her."

Meanwhile, Henry reluctantly prepared to sail for Korea alone in the autumn.

We packed again, we who were to stay behind, this time to move to Lancaster, near my brother. Henry felt this would be best because he wouldn't be there to care for us. Alice helped with folding the linens and sorting the younger children's toys. She grew stronger every day. I believe the change began when she realized that her family, most of it, would stay longer with her and not abandon her to strangers. Henry booked to sail for Korea on September 12th from San Francisco.

Meanwhile we went to the Appenzeller farm in Souderton, Pennsylvania, to spend some time. Dear Henry turned as brown as a Korean farmer for he worked in the hay fields, drove the horses, even milked cows. He brought in from the garden huge baskets full of vegetables, which the children and I had to peel or shell, but we all ate platefuls of whatever he brought in, and I took delight in the brown skin, hearty laughter, and relaxed spirits of those I loved. Henry looked so good with some meat on his bones and he coaxed me each evening to sit in the porch swing with him where we watched the moon come up while the children chased fireflies.

September came far too soon. Henry boarded the train to Chicago and then on to San Francisco; the children and I moved to our rented home in Lancaster. All four of them went to public school. Alice was delighted to live at home. I knew that what we were doing was for the best and God surprised me with peace about the separation.

Just before he boarded the train, Henry and I went to visit his parents' graves and, as we stood there gazing at the stones, the dear man spoke of his mother: "She always believed something terrible would happen to me in Korea, remember? Surely heaven has given her a better outlook on our calling, don't you think?"

I drew breath to reply but he crushed me in a huge hug and the breath I'd drawn left me, unused. Henry's strong, brown arms at that moment gave me such a sense of safety and love. We looked into each other's eyes for a long moment.

"Go with God, my darling," I said.

His arms tightened about me. "That's my Ella," he said. "Guard our children and yourself. I'll not be whole again until all of you are with me, so come as soon as possible."

Our eyes swam in tears so all I did was nod. We turned and left the little country cemetery, hand in hand.

Chapter 26

Without Him

We began to receive letters from Henry late in October. They trickled in to our mailbox; first were the letters he wrote on board ship. He wrote each day to one of the children or to me and mailed a batch of them in Honolulu. I was surprised and touched by the way he carefully communicated with each of us, one by one, a lovely indication of the depth and breadth of his love. He suggested we plan to stop in Hawaii on our way back to Korea for he found it beautiful and wanted us to enjoy it, too. He seemed hungry for news of us all, and I hoped our letters would begin to reach him soon.

From the ship he wrote, "I feel more and more as distance increases between us that I need you and want you and yet feel sure that it is for the best to be where you are. Take good care of yourself and keep well."

To little Henry of course he had some fatherly exhortations. "I wonder how you are spending your Saturdays. Your idea of getting something suitable to do is very good and I hope you have succeeded. Henry made friends with the boy who swept out Cooper's Market and wanted to earn money, too.) You may have to make several attempts before you come on something you like and is suitable. Your first work, however, is your books and those you must not neglect. Do not be discouraged if you fail to find at once what you and Mama are after. You will find it if you keep on."

I suppose I should've stopped calling our son "Little Henry" by then. He was as tall as I was, and his father wasn't there to create confusion over who was big and who was little. But that all took car of itself soon enough, I'm afraid.

In Mary's letter, mailed from Chemulpo in Korea, her father tol about sailing through a typhoon just off Japan. They sheltered behin an island but left it too soon and the waves nearly swamped the ship, which made Henry impatient, it seems. "This way of travelin makes the trip from Kobe to Chemulpo too long. I fear we shall nc reach Pusan by tomorrow morning. Are you going to school ever day? Do you like it? Who is your teacher? Are you helping Mama a you can? I want so much to hear from you but will have to wait som days yet. Goodbye, and be a good little girl."

Then he finally did reach Korea. "Everywhere and by everybod the most earnest inquiries after you and the children are made. 'Ho' is Alice? Hope she is better. So sorry to hear she had such a hard time The interest is genuine and I am very grateful and deeply touched."

To Alice: "At our service here last Sunday Esther Kim Pak wante me to meet her sister. She told me she was just your age, born in th same year."

I was glad to learn he took at least a short time for recreation. "W had tennis today. I was up at the school in my office when Bunke came with his tennis suit on and wanted me to come on, reinforcin this request by promising to knock me out on the first round. Thi was too great an inducement not to accept. I went down as soo as I could. Bunker and Mr. Frampton, the English teacher in th government school, were having a single. No one else was around t play but they called Hulburt who appeared with his usual buoyanc of spirit. He and I took them and got to 5-2 in our favor. We let u a trifle on them, had a 5-all set, which our opponents took. We ha a splendid set-to and we did love it. "Loulie invited me for a cup c tea but I thanked her, came back home and took a ride to the Korea post office on my wheel, getting home a little before six o'clock. Yo see, my life is much as it was when we were all together. I am a' alone, which may account for the length of this letter."

The idea of Henry playing tennis with the other men pleased m greatly. He so needed some variety in his life to offset the endles hours of work with school and church. I knew he was lonely in ou house all by himself, even though he didn't mention it much. He didn't want to make us sad, I knew.

Ida received her own letter written in November: "This is the fourth anniversary of the assumption of the title of emperor by His Majesty. Mr. Bunker and I went to the palace to attend the celebration. We saw quite a few new foreign faces there. I saw Miss Sontag through the window and she bowed. *(I didn't know her. She may have been a fellow passenger with Henry on board ship.)* She looks rather bad. On Mr. Gifford's old place here in Chungdong, a 30,000 yen hotel is going up. *(Yen is Japanese money, so I presumed it was being built by a Japanese company.)* It is to be the Imperial Hotel and Miss Sontag will have charge of it. I rode on my bike to the foreign cemetery after I came from the palace. The day was pleasant and the ride a nice change. I hope you are all well."

The children and I survived, just barely, the Christmas holidays without their father. People at church were most kind, showering us with gifts and including us in their celebrations, but nothing filled the gap that Henry left. The lovely and helpful gifts we received from family and friends were almost overwhelming when held up against what we usually gave and received in Korea. But we missed the camaraderie of our co-workers, working to decorate our homes and put together a festive meal with whatever we could find in South Gate market.

"I am so awfully busy," Henry had written in November and we'd just received, "that I shall have little time to think of being alone. At night I long to see the children and you. Even a row would not be entirely unwelcome as it would at least bring you all to me and me to you." How sad-sweet to think he'd even welcome a fuss if it meant we were together again.

Of course he fell into his old, too-busy ways: "Sunday passed as usual. Attended Sunday school and preaching in First Church in the morning. Hastened to the East Gate at 2 P.M., attended the foreign service in the school chapel at 3:30, had a long visit with Dr. Avison after the service here, and held the evening meeting at 6:30. A busy day. Received five women on probation in the morning, and they gave me a dinner last night where I made quite a lengthy speech."

He wrote to Alice on her 16th birthday, recalling that a year ago we celebrated her 15th on the Mediterranean Sea: "I saw Helen Hulbur on the street riding a bicycle and she said to me, 'Doesn't this bicycle look fine?' *(Good grief, that dreadful fussed-over bicycle...and now he was admiring it! All was forgiven and forgotten, I guess.)* I hope you will persuade Mama to bring a wheel. Henry and Ida can use it. Everybody rides here."

He scolded Ida for not writing him: "Brace up and let me see how you can write. I wonder where you are, what you are doing. Be good, helpful and kind. Have you seen the Bible I sent you from Chicago? How do you like it?" I think all of us enjoyed Henry's admonition to each one. They gave us just a small sense of having our father and husband with us, in the natural place he wanted to be.

"Henry wrote to us almost every day and we all enjoyed his letters, but I found it difficult to read the letter he wrote on New Year's Eve. We all were sniffing before I finished. He reminisced about the past year, speaking of Alice's long sickness that, he said, "I hope is sanctified to our good." He also talked of our visits here and there while he was still in America, especially our time at the Appenzeller farm in Souderton.

"We have been separated for nearly four months. We need to remind ourselves continually that time is passing by rapidly. Alice is over 16 when only a few years ago she was carried around by me. Even Mary, while she remains the baby, is getting to be a big girl of almost nine years.

"Improve your moments and hours every one. Live as unto the Lord and do everything as in His immediate presence and to His honor and glory. I will try to do the same. The year 1902 will be an important one to us all. We have before us much work to do.

"It is now nearly time for our watchnight service. I shall pray for you. Above everything else I shall ask God to lead us to do His will perfectly and follow Him unreservedly in all things. May He have you in His holy keeping. Trust Him. Have faith in Him. Write much. With tender love to one and all, and a happy new year. Papa."

New Year is the most important holiday on the Korean calendar, with multiple receptions, new clothes, festive food and greetings especially to the high and mighty among us. Henry told Ida about the emperor's New Year's audience, a stand-around event where everyone there kept an eye out to see who else was invited and hoped for an opportunity to bow before the emperor. Then he wrote, "I wonder how you spent Christmas and New Year's. I confess that I want to see you very much sometimes and this first day of the year seems one of those times. I made a lot of calls in the afternoon, riding my bike."

Spring came to Lancaster by April. Pennsylvania's bright green hills stretched on and on in beauty and peace. I liked to walk to the edge of town after dinner with the children. We often pretended we were going to South Gate and made up stories as if we were there, what we saw in the market, around the gate and out under the pine trees beyond the wall. At times one of them brought along a friend who found it hard to understand what in the world we were talking about.

Henry wrote that as soon as PaiJai closed for summer recess, he and the rest of the Bible translation committee would assemble down south in Mokpo for some concentrated daily work sessions, a seemingly innocent and useful next step toward the all-important goal of getting the Bible into the hands of Koreans. None of us knew what else that trip would mean to us.

Henry sent news of Soon Hee who went to work for Mrs. Scranton. "She gives off a quiet glow, your special friend, and she spends all her free time reading in what she calls simply 'The Book.' God's love has transformed her life, Ella, and her appearance. Remember how she looked that day you dragged her in from the compound gate? Hair all a-tangle and bedraggled, dirty silk court garments. And skinny as a stray cat! But now? Her hair is sleek and smooth, fastened with a silver pin, a gift from Mrs. Scranton, I'm told. Her long Korean dress is a quiet blue. She looks the perfect picture of a modest Korean lady

"Take great joy, my dear, in your treasure. Soon Hee is a perfect example of the transformation that can come when a lost one is found by the Savior. Please forgive me for opposing you the day you brought her into our house.

"Oh, I almost forgot to tell you. Soon Hee wants to return to her village and her family. She wants to tell them of her faith and hopes they will accept Jesus into their lives as she has done. She tells me she comes from a place not too far from Mokpo, so I suggested she accompany my teacher and me on the journey and we can see her safely home."

***

In June the unthinkable, the unimaginable hit me in the face and broke my heart beyond repair.

Henry Appenzeller was dead. My dear Henry, gone. Neither the children nor I could believe it, but the letter from the New York office lay on my desk. It quoted a cable they received from Korea. He had drowned. We had no body, no grave, no memorial stone. Our little Ida kept saying, "It isn't true! Mama, it isn't true. It can't be!"

She stayed close to my side through the memorial service that the children and I planned together, huge tears running down her cheeks. Little Henry—no, he was the only Henry now, no longer little—walked beside me into church with the three girls following, directed his sisters to precede us into the pew and then sat on the aisle, just as his father would have done. I glanced at his set, white face and my heart broke all over again. No more father to guide him. Was it enough, what Henry already did to form and train his son?

In time, letters came from Korea, giving us all the details of what happened to the man of our home and our hearts. Until they did, we waited and wept and tried to learn how to live without him.

Yes, they came, the letters, and even though we read them hungrily, our hearts hurt all over again with each dreadful fact, each oving thought from our friends. Horace Allen's wife, Fannie, the woman who was so silent, so remote and so hard to know told it all best. For safe keeping I put her letter in with Henry's papers and diaries that he left here.

Because decent roads were all but non-existent in Korea, it seems that my husband was traveling to Mokpo by coastal steamer, much faster and smoother than whatever road there may have been, to attend the translation committee meeting. His teacher and Soon Hee were also on board, Soon Hee going home at last to tell her family about her acceptance of Christianity.

In the night Henry's ship collided with another and sank so quickly that almost no one was rescued. Someone wrote, I can't think how who it was, that Henry was last seen racing along the corridor to rescue Soon Hee and his teacher but all three of them were lost. I can't quite accept that was the way of it because Henry always slept so soundly. I had to pry him out of bed whenever I heard noises at night. More likely it seems to me he never wakened until he opened his eyes in heaven. At least that is what I want to believe. An awful part of the whole story is the fact that Henry's mother had been predicting just such a tragedy for years before it happened, and we brushed her off, giving her bad dreams no credence at all. I ponder this in my heart and can find no rhyme or reason, and certainly no solace in the knowledge that her fearful predictions were true.

Henry always loved a translation of a Korean poem done by James Gale because it is an inquiry by an absent husband about his family. Because he can't say so directly, he asks about the plum tree by the door instead. It goes:

"Have you seen my native land?
Can you tell me all you know?
Did just before the old home door
The plum tree blossom show?
The stranger answers at once,
They were in bloom, tho' pale, tis true,
And sad from waiting long for you".

How many times through the years I grew sad and pale, and angry, too, at Henry's absences. Life never felt comfortable or safe

when he wasn't there. From this journey, however, he would no
return so the children and I had to make the best of it. A conversatio
some months after Henry's death with Alice, our first baby no
approaching adulthood, helped with my perspective.

"Mother," she began, "I'm remembering how much you and Pap
liked to walk over to South Gate back in Seoul. We children did, too

A surge of pain puddled tears in my eyes as I nodded in agreemen
"Yes, she was like an old friend to me. She had already stood fo
centuries before I rode through her for the first time and I'm sure sh
will be there for a long time to come."

"I would like to see her again." Alice surprised me with such
wish. After all, Korea's tension and turmoil had threatened her healt
to such an extreme that it wouldn't have surprised me to hear her sa
she wanted nothing further to do with that country.

"Perhaps you will," I said. "Your life lies out before you. There
always work to do for God in Korea, and if He calls, you can go. An
I'm sure He wouldn't mind just a visit, either."

As I talked with Alice, I knew in my heart that Korea and Sout
Gate were no longer a part of my life. There would be no more friendl
guards, no more noisy market for me. I knew I'd moved on in m
pilgrimage, or had been moved by Henry's death. But forget her
Never! She played a role in my life representing strength, stability
protection even, and these qualities remained with me—even beyon
South Gate.

Afterword

Alice Appenzeller's history of childhood illness took a turn for the better as she settled into life in Lancaster, Pennsylvania, her parents' hometown. Ella sent her eldest daughter to Miss Stahr's School for girls, eventually known as Lancaster Country Day School. She graduated in 1905 and then enrolled in Wellesley College.

During her college years, Alice found the stamina to sing in the choir, volunteer for a lengthy list of good deeds, and maintain relationships with an abundance of friends, as well as studying. On graduation from Wellesley, she returned to her old school in Lancaster, joining the faculty there as teacher of German and history. (Ella must have smiled to herself, thinking how pleased Henry would have been to see his daughter following in his educational footsteps.)

But her story doesn't end there, not at all. In a Wellesley-produced article called "Person of the Week," the author said Alice's "religious vocation was strong, as was her love for her childhood home in Korea." In 1915, she was appointed by the Methodist Church as "a missionary teacher at the Ewha Kindergarten School in Seoul." Mary Scranton's living room school for girls, flourishing over the years, pulled Alice back "home." In spite of all the difficulties she'd known in Korea as a girl, she took up the opportunities her parents had pursued with such energy and commitment a few decades earlier.

Within three years, Alice was made principal of Ewha primary and high schools—no small assignment, certainly—and by October of 1922, she became President of Ewha College. The Wellesley article tells us "she had spent the earlier months of 1922 earning a master's degree at Columbia University Teachers' College in New York City and returned to New York in 1927 and 1930 for further graduate work."

Alice Appenzeller obviously matured into a healthy woman with gifts and goals aplenty. Dim black-and-white photos of her in academic garb taken in those days show her tall and smiling. If you look closely, you can see a strong, square jaw that resembles her father's, which her mother fell in love with long ago.

Ewha was Korea's first college for women and soon was educating 400 or more students. Alice, it turns out, was not only spiritual and intellectual, but also a skilled administrator and leader as well, adding property and buildings as the school expanded, and persuading the Korean government to accredit Ewha as a college in 1925. She had furloughs as a Methodist missionary, as did her parents, and she dedicated her time in the U.S. to fund-raising for Ewha, an incessant necessity for all schools, it seems.

In 1935, Korea honored Alice with a Blue Ribbon medal, the highest honor given to women at the time. Clearly, Ewha women's university had national attention and approval. On the other side of the Pacific Ocean, in 1937, she received an honorary Doctor of Pedagogy from Boston University.

By then World War II was intruding, so Alice was evacuated along with other foreigners and spent the early war years with friends. In 1942, however, she went to Hawaii to teach religion in the Korean Methodist community.

As soon as the bombs stopped falling and the dust cleared, however, Alice was back at work in her beloved Ewha. But her time there would prove short. In 1950, Alice Appenzeller stood to lead the university's chapel service when she collapsed and died behind th pulpit, her ministry interrupted far too soon, many would say, as they did when her father, Henry, drowned in a shipwreck on his way to a Bible translation committee meeting.

She would have liked what her alma mater's reunion record book said in 1950, in speaking of her death: "Most of South Korea's prominent women leaders are Ewha graduates." Alice is buried in the foreigner's cemetery where also stands a monument honoring her father, Henry Appenzeller.

About the Author

Carroll Ferguson Rader grew up on a farm in Ohio, daughter of an itinerant evangelist. Since infancy, therefore, she's been a veteran of revivals, camp meetings, and Sunday night evangelistic meetings.

Carroll is an alumnus of Asbury University, where she majored in church music. She and her husband of 40-plus years, Dr. Everett Hunt, spent more than 35 years in cross-cultural ministry with One Mission Society, more than 20 years of that time in Seoul, South Korea. While in South Korea, Carroll taught English to pastors and other leaders, worked in the mission office, and helped people in ministry develop skills in writing in English as a second language. She worked in the Billy Graham team office prior to and during the Seoul crusade and also wrote the script for a Ken Anderson film when they worked in Korea.

Carroll has written several books as well as magazine articles for *OMS Outreach, Decision, Christian Life, Campus Crusade*, Sunday newspaper supplemental magazines, and a column for her hometown newspaper. She received an Evangelical Press Association award for an article she wrote for *Outreach* magazine. Her previous works include:

- *From the Claws of the Dragon*, 1988, Zondervan Publishing (trans. into Chinese, Spanish, and Portuguese), paperback
- *Absolutely! Can We Know What's Right or Wrong?* with Vicki Lake, 1990, Zondervan Publishing, paperback
- *"Who's Got the Baby Jesus?," "The Critter Keeper,"* 1995, Lillenas Publishing, Christmas Program Builder No. 48
- *"Visitors at the Palace,"* 1998, Lillenas Publishing, Christmas Program Builder No. 51
- *If Two Shall Agree*, 2001, Beacon Hill Press, a biography of Salvation Army General, Paul Rader, and his wife, Commissioner Kay, paperback
- *Of Guts and Grace—Fifty Years of Men for Missions of OMS*, 2004, OMS, paperback

Carroll lives now in Greenwood, Indiana, to be near her daughter, who was born in Korea.

CPSIA information can be obtained at www.ICGtesting.com
Printed in the USA
LVOW10s2026010813

345755LV00002B/5/P